C000019446

Fad Free Recipes
- 50 Real Food Recipes for Under 500 Calories

© Weight Loss Resources 2014

Published by:

Weight Loss Resources Ltd

2C Flag Business Exchange

Vicarage Farm Road

Peterborough

PE1 5TX.

Tel: 01733 345592

www.weightlossresources.co.uk

ISBN 978-1-904512-13-4

Authors: Rebecca Walton and Laurence Beeken

Design and Layout: Joanne Putney

Printed and bound by:

Bookprintinguk.com, Peterborough PE2 9BF

Contents

Introduction

The Recipes

The Desserts

Lose Weight the Easy Way

Imagine being told that the best diet to help you lose weight includes all of your favourite meals and snacks. Imagine too that you can still enjoy your weekend glass of wine and your indulgent chocolate snack.

That's where Weight Loss Resources' "Fad Free Recipes" comes in.

Here at WeightLossResources.co.uk, we know that dieting is NOT about depriving yourself and eating nothing but endless salads and cardboard snacks. It's more about making healthy choices in what we eat, the amount we eat and how we cook.

Over the years, feedback from members of our online programme; www.weightlossresources.co.uk has highlighted that sometimes all of us need a bit of guidance, whether it's every day, where to start or when you're stuck for ideas on what to have for lunch or dinner for under 500 calories.

So that's what we've done for you. You'll find 50 easy to make, calorie counted meals that have been put together with one thing in mind – to help you cut calories without compromising your lifestyle. Plus, to make sure that you don't feel like you're "on a diet", we've also included a range of tasty desserts and a handy list of calorie counted snacks for when you fancy a treat.

Why Calorie Counting?

Over the last few years, an endless conveyor belt of faddy diets which cut carbs, boost protein or skip entire food groups have made losing weight a much more complicated process.

Add to this an increasing number of celebrities and 'experts' who have convinced us that dieting is all about restriction and denial – is it any wonder that more and more of us don't know where to turn for healthy and interesting meal ideas?

According to the British Nutrition Foundation

> *"To lose weight, the energy intake from food must be less than the energy output".*

This is why calorie counting is the most effective weight loss method. It goes straight to the heart of the problem - no fad diets, pills or special eating plans are necessary.

Losing weight through calorie counting is relatively easy. You won't have to put normal life on hold while following a calorie controlled diet. Added benefits are that calorie counting raises your awareness of what your body needs; it educates you about what's in what you eat, and helps you learn how to eat healthily for life.

How Many Calories Do You Need?

Factors that affect your personal daily calorie requirement include your age, height and weight, your basic level of daily activity, and your body composition.

In order to lose weight you need to eat fewer calories per day than your body needs. To lose 1lb a week you need a negative calorie balance of 500 calories per day. To lose weight at 2lb a week you need to reduce your calorie intake by 1000 calories per day.

Take a look at our reference tables on pages 8 and 9 to see how many calories you need per day.

Calories Required to Maintain Weight
Adult Females

ACTIVITY LEVEL / AGE

	VERY SEDENTARY			MODERATELY SEDENTARY			MODERATELY ACTIVE			VERY ACTIVE		
	<30	30-60	60+	<30	30-60	60+	<30	30-60	60+	<30	30-60	60+
7st 7	1425	1473	1304	1544	1596	1412	1781	1841	1630	2138	2210	1956
8st 0	1481	1504	1338	1605	1629	1450	1852	1880	1673	2222	2256	2008
8st 7	1537	1535	1373	1666	1663	1487	1922	1919	1716	2306	2302	2059
9st 0	1594	1566	1407	1726	1696	1524	1992	1957	1759	2391	2349	2111
9st 7	1650	1596	1442	1787	1729	1562	2062	1996	1802	2475	2395	2163
10st 0	1706	1627	1476	1848	1763	1599	2133	2034	1845	2559	2441	2214
10st 7	1762	1658	1511	1909	1796	1637	2203	2073	1888	2644	2487	2266
11st 0	1819	1689	1545	1970	1830	1674	2273	2111	1931	2728	2534	2318
11st 7	1875	1720	1580	2031	1863	1711	2344	2150	1975	2813	2580	2370
12st 0	1931	1751	1614	2092	1897	1749	2414	2188	2018	2897	2626	2421
12st 7	1987	1781	1648	2153	1930	1786	2484	2227	2061	2981	2672	2473
13st 0	2044	1812	1683	2214	1963	1823	2555	2266	2104	3066	2719	2525
13st 7	2100	1843	1717	2275	1997	1861	2625	2304	2147	3150	2765	2576
14st 0	2156	1874	1752	2336	2030	1898	2695	2343	2190	3234	2811	2628
14st 7	2212	1905	1786	2397	2064	1935	2766	2381	2233	3319	2858	2680
15st 0	2269	1936	1821	2458	2097	1973	2836	2420	2276	3403	2904	2732
15st 7	2325	1967	1855	2519	2130	2010	2906	2458	2319	3488	2950	2783
16st 0	2381	1997	1890	2580	2164	2047	2976	2497	2362	3572	2996	2835
16st 7	2437	2028	1924	2640	2197	2085	3047	2535	2405	3656	3043	2887
17st 0	2494	2059	1959	2701	2231	2122	3117	2574	2449	3741	3089	2938
17st 7	2550	2090	1993	2762	2264	2159	3187	2613	2492	3825	3135	2990
18st 0	2606	2121	2028	2823	2298	2197	3258	2651	2535	3909	3181	3042
18st 7	2662	2152	2062	2884	2331	2234	3328	2690	2578	3994	3228	3093
19st 0	2719	2182	2097	2945	2364	2271	3398	2728	2621	4078	3274	3145
19st 7	2775	2213	2131	3006	2398	2309	3469	2767	2664	4162	3320	3197
20st 0	2831	2244	2166	3067	2431	2346	3539	2805	2707	4247	3366	3249
20st 7	2887	2275	2200	3128	2465	2383	3609	2844	2750	4331	3413	3300
21st 0	2944	2306	2235	3189	2498	2421	3680	2882	2793	4416	3459	3352
21st 7	3000	2337	2269	3250	2531	2458	3750	2921	2836	4500	3505	3404
22st 0	3056	2368	2303	3311	2565	2495	3820	2960	2879	4584	3552	3455
22st 7	3112	2398	2338	3372	2598	2533	3890	2998	2923	4669	3598	3507
23st 0	3169	2429	2372	3433	2632	2570	3961	3037	2966	4753	3644	3559
23st 7	3225	2460	2407	3494	2665	2608	4031	3075	3009	4837	3690	3611
24st 0	3281	2491	2441	3554	2699	2645	4101	3114	3052	4922	3737	3662
24st 7	3337	2522	2476	3615	2732	2682	4172	3152	3095	5006	3783	3714
25st 0	3394	2553	2510	3676	2765	2720	4242	3191	3138	5091	3829	3766
25st 7	3450	2583	2545	3737	2799	2757	4312	3229	3181	5175	3875	3817
26st 0	3506	2614	2579	3798	2832	2794	4383	3268	3224	5259	3922	3869
26st 7	3562	2645	2614	3859	2866	2832	4453	3307	3267	5344	3968	3921
27st 0	3618	2676	2648	3920	2899	2869	4523	3345	3310	5428	4014	3973
27st 7	3675	2707	2683	3981	2932	2906	4594	3384	3353	5512	4060	4024
28st 0	3731	2738	2717	4042	2966	2944	4664	3422	3397	5597	4107	4076
28st 7	3787	2768	2752	4103	2999	2981	4734	3461	3440	5681	4153	4128

WEIGHT IN STONES / LBS

Calories Required to Maintain Weight
Adult Males

ACTIVITY LEVEL / AGE

WEIGHT IN STONES / LBS	VERY SEDENTARY			MODERATELY SEDENTARY			MODERATELY ACTIVE			VERY ACTIVE		
	<30	30-60	60+	<30	30-60	60+	<30	30-60	60+	<30	30-60	60+
9st 0	1856	1827	1502	2010	1979	1627	2320	2284	1878	2784	2741	2254
9st 7	1913	1871	1547	2072	2026	1676	2391	2338	1933	2870	2806	2320
10st 0	1970	1914	1591	2134	2074	1724	2463	2393	1989	2955	2871	2387
10st 7	2027	1958	1636	2196	2121	1772	2534	2447	2045	3041	2937	2454
11st 0	2084	2001	1680	2258	2168	1820	2605	2502	2100	3127	3002	2520
11st 7	2141	2045	1724	2320	2215	1868	2677	2556	2156	3212	3067	2587
12st 0	2199	2088	1769	2382	2262	1916	2748	2611	2211	3298	3133	2654
12st 7	2256	2132	1813	2444	2310	1965	2820	2665	2267	3384	3198	2720
13st 0	2313	2175	1858	2506	2357	2013	2891	2719	2322	3470	3263	2787
13st 7	2370	2219	1902	2568	2404	2061	2963	2774	2378	3555	3329	2854
14st 0	2427	2262	1947	2630	2451	2109	3034	2828	2434	3641	3394	2920
14st 7	2484	2306	1991	2691	2498	2157	3106	2883	2489	3727	3459	2987
15st 0	2542	2350	2036	2753	2545	2205	3177	2937	2545	3813	3525	3054
15st 7	2599	2393	2080	2815	2593	2253	3248	2992	2600	3898	3590	3120
16st 0	2656	2437	2125	2877	2640	2302	3320	3046	2656	3984	3655	3187
16st 7	2713	2480	2169	2939	2687	2350	3391	3100	2711	4070	3721	3254
17st 0	2770	2524	2213	3001	2734	2398	3463	3155	2767	4155	3786	3320
17st 7	2827	2567	2258	3063	2781	2446	3534	3209	2823	4241	3851	3387
18st 0	2884	2611	2302	3125	2828	2494	3606	3264	2878	4327	3917	3454
18st 7	2942	2654	2347	3187	2876	2542	3677	3318	2934	4413	3982	3520
19st 0	2999	2698	2391	3249	2923	2591	3749	3373	2989	4498	4047	3587
19st 7	3056	2741	2436	3311	2970	2639	3820	3427	3045	4584	4112	3654
20st 0	3113	2785	2480	3373	3017	2687	3891	3481	3100	4670	4178	3721
20st 7	3170	2829	2525	3434	3064	2735	3963	3536	3156	4756	4243	3787
21st 0	3227	2872	2569	3496	3112	2783	4034	3590	3211	4841	4308	3854
21st 7	3285	2916	2614	3558	3159	2831	4106	3645	3267	4927	4374	3921
22st 0	3342	2959	2658	3620	3206	2880	4177	3699	3323	5013	4439	3987
22st 7	3399	3003	2702	3682	3253	2928	4249	3754	3378	5098	4504	4054
23st 0	3456	3046	2747	3744	3300	2976	4320	3808	3434	5184	4570	4121
23st 7	3513	3090	2791	3806	3347	3024	4392	3862	3489	5270	4635	4187
24st 0	3570	3133	2836	3868	3395	3072	4463	3917	3545	5356	4700	4254
24st 7	3627	3177	2880	3930	3442	3120	4534	3971	3600	5441	4766	4321
25st 0	3685	3220	2925	3992	3489	3168	4606	4026	3656	5527	4831	4387
25st 7	3742	3264	2969	4054	3536	3217	4677	4080	3712	5613	4896	4454
26st 0	3799	3308	3014	4116	3583	3265	4749	4135	3767	5699	4962	4521
26st 7	3856	3351	3058	4177	3630	3313	4820	4189	3823	5784	5027	4587
27st 0	3913	3395	3103	4239	3678	3361	4892	4243	3878	5870	5092	4654
27st 7	3970	3438	3147	4301	3725	3409	4963	4298	3934	5956	5158	4721
28st 0	4028	3482	3191	4363	3772	3457	5035	4352	3989	6042	5223	4787
28st 7	4085	3525	3236	4425	3819	3506	5106	4407	4045	6127	5288	4854
29st 0	4142	3569	3280	4487	3866	3554	5177	4461	4101	6213	5354	4921
29st 7	4199	3612	3325	4549	3913	3602	5249	4516	4156	6299	5419	4987
30st 0	4256	3656	3369	4611	3961	3650	5320	4570	4212	6384	5484	5054

8 Simple Tips for Cutting Calories in Your Everyday Cooking

Fortunately, it's not too difficult to reduce the amount of calories that you are eating. Making small changes to the way you cook can cut your calories without depriving yourself of the things you love to eat! Here's how...

1. Grill, boil, bake, poach or steam wherever possible.

This avoids adding unnecessary fats to your meal, and considering that a tablespoon of oil is around 130 calories this can be a massive win. If you're grilling or roasting meat remember to put the meat on a wire rack to allow excess fat to run off.

2. If you do need to use oil, use spray oils!

Swapping regular oils for spray versions wherever you can will make a big difference to the calorie counts of meals. A few sprays of oil come in at less than 10 calories! (Remember a tablespoon of regular oil is around 130 cals).

3. Choose boiled or baked potatoes.

Potatoes make up a large part of our diet here in the UK, and they're a great source of carbohydrate - try to avoid potatoes cooked with added fat and go 'au natural' with the humble spud.

4. Remove visible fat from meats and remove the skin from chicken before cooking.

Fat contains 9 calories per gram (the highest of all the nutrients), and although we need some fats in our diet cutting away the excess will help to keep calorie counts low.

5. Avoid processed, fatty meat products.

Things like sausages and cheap burgers have high calorie and fat content without giving you the goodness you get from simple, pure protein sources. Avoid them, or get the best you can with your budget for better quality ingredients and nutrition.

6. Use semi-skimmed or skimmed milk and reduced calorie/fat yoghurts, soft cheese and crème fraiche etc.

Dairy products are an important part of our diet and there are some good quality low calorie versions around now. Make sure you check the labels and look out for added sugars. When using hard cheese in a dish go for mature or strong varieties - they give you more flavour while using less of the product. Grating cheese where possible will also mean that you use less.

7. Swap creamy sauces for vegetable based sauces/stocks.

Whether cooking from scratch or buying in jars. Don't forget the power of sweet chilli, soy and Worcester sauces to add flavour to your cooking for very few calories!

8. Pile up on veg!

Vegetables and salads are a great way to bulk out meals without ramping up the calorie count. Whether fresh or frozen make sure you have plenty of veg on your plate to help you feel fuller without breaking the calorie bank.

Control Your Portions

As well as making some smart food swaps, you'll also need to watch your serving sizes, just reducing your portions will help shift those pounds.

Even foods perceived as 'healthy' contain calories so you may need to limit the amount that you eat. When you start out, weigh your portions rather than using a 'guestimated' weight, that way you can calculate the calories content accurately.

Successful slimmers agree that making sure your portions are the right size is one of the most important things you can do to help with your weight loss efforts. Take a look at our 10 'tricks of the trade' to help you keep your serving sizes in check without feeling deprived.

10 Simple Ways to Reduce Your Portion Sizes

1. Drink a glass of water before eating

You'll fill your stomach more quickly and be less inclined to overload your plate. Plus you may actually be feeling thirsty rather than hungry.

2. Bulk up with veggies

Add more veggies or salad to your plate and you'll not be able to add so much of the more calorie dense foods such as pasta or meats. Plus, the fibre will help you to feel fuller for longer.

3. Use a smaller plate

Your plate will look fuller and more satisfying and you'll be able to add far less and instantly cut down on the portion size.

4. Use smaller cutlery

If you can't fit so much on your fork or spoon, it will take longer to eat and you'll feeler fuller before you've finished your meal.

5. Serve your meal directly to your plate

You'll eat far less than if you dish up from a serving bowl at the table.

6. Learn to throw uneaten portions away

Or stick them in the freezer before you sit down to eat - it's wasted whether it's in the bin or round your middle.

7. Don't eat from the bag

Place a small amount of your favourite snack into a small cereal bowl and put the packet away - people tend to be less aware of portion size when they snack directly from the pack.

8. Use a food diary to learn how many calories are in the portion you are actually eating

Then make a conscious decision to eat less of it.

9. Mentally compare portions with everyday objects

For example a portion of meat should be no bigger than a deck of cards, cheese no bigger than a matchbox, potatoes, rice or pasta no bigger than a tennis ball; and butter no more than a postage stamp.

10. Avoid 'family size' ready meals and snacks

Go for the regular sized servings, 300-400g for ready meals and 25g for crisps.

The Snacks

Snacks are an integral part of any eating plan – they provide a 'top up' when you need it and a treat when you crave it.

All of our snacks have been calorie counted to make sure that you know exactly what you're eating and you can mix and match whatever takes your fancy.

100 Calorie Snacks

- 3 Tbsp reduced-fat hummus with crudités

- 1 apple, 1 kiwi fruit and 1 satsuma

- 2 chocolate chip cookies

- 2 whole-wheat crackers with 2 Tbsp of low-fat soft cheese

- 1 small glass of red or dry white wine

- 1 small packet of Skips

- 1 bowl of fresh fruit salad with 1 Tbsp single cream

150 Calorie Snacks

- 1 small banana, 1 apple and 1 satsuma

- 2-finger Kit Kat and 1 sachet reduced-fat hot chocolate drink

- Strawberry shake: blend 150ml/1/4pt semi-skimmed milk, 1 small pot diet strawberry yoghurt and 8 fresh strawberries

- 1 slice wholemeal toast topped with 2 Tsp peanut butter and 1 Tsp jam

- 1 slice honeydew melon with 2 slices lean Parma ham

- 4tbsp bran flakes with semi-skimmed milk

- ½ small avocado with 1 tomato, 25g/1oz reduced-fat mozzarella cheese, balsamic vinegar and fresh basil.

200 Calorie Snacks

- Chop 1 kiwi fruit, 1 small banana and 1 satsuma. Top with 1 small pot diet fromage frais and 1 Tbsp chopped mixed nuts.

- 2 toasted crumpets with 2tsp low-fat spread and a scrape of Marmite,

- 1 wholemeal pitta bread filled with 3 Tbsp reduced-calorie coleslaw and salad.

- 1 toasted teacake with 2 Tsp low-fat spread.

- 1 wholemeal fruit scone with 2 Tsp low-fat spread.

- 2 slices wholemeal toast with 2 Tsp low-fat spread and Marmite.

The Recipes

Since we don't want to sacrifice taste in the name of 'calorie counting', you'll find all of our recipes have been put together to make sure that they stay as close as possible to proper home cooking – no fancy substitutes or no fat alternatives.

We've simply taken our favourite recipes and tweaked them to reduce the calories while keeping all of the taste.

All of our recipes show you in plain terms the amount of calories, carbs, protein, and fat, per portion, along with sugar and saturated fats.

You'll also see that they detail the number of servings which can easily be adapted for your needs – cook for yourself, your family or for a dinner party!

Recipes are ordered by the total time it takes to prepare and cook them – from the quickest in the first few pages to those that take a little longer later on.

A simple favourite that can be knocked up really quickly.
Perfect when asparagus is in season in the spring.

Griddled Asparagus
with Poached Egg and Bacon

Serves 1 • **Prep** 5 mins • **Cook** 10 mins

INGREDIENTS

Asparagus - Trimmed	8 Spears/145g
Medium Egg	1 Egg/58g
Olive Oil	½ Tbsp
Back Bacon - Visible Fat Removed	2 Rashers/50g
Fresh Chives - Finely Chopped	1 Tsp
Salt	1 Pinch
Black Pepper	1 Pinch
Butter	10g

NUTRITION INFO per Serving

Cals	Protein	Carbs	Sugar	Fat	Sat Fat	Fibre	Fruit and Veg
344	28g	3g	2.6g	24.5g	9.1g	2.6g	1.9

METHOD

1. Pre heat a griddle or frying pan to a medium-high heat with the olive oil and the butter. Bring a pan of water to a simmer. Turn on the grill.

2. Place the bacon under the grill and cook until crispy on the edges (remember to turn it half way through).

3. While the bacon cooks, griddle the asparagus for 4-5 minutes until tender, keeping the asparagus moving.

4. Break and drop the egg into the pan of simmering water and poach for 3 minutes for a runny yolk, or 5-6 minutes for a firmer yolk. Remove and drain on kitchen paper.

5. Arrange the asparagus on your plate and drizzle over any remaining butter/oil from the pan. Serve the egg and bacon on top, seasoned with a pinch of salt and pepper, and sprinkle with the chopped chives.

This recipe is great to use with any leftover roast chicken (or pork!). If you don't have any leftovers then buy pre roasted chicken breasts.

Chicken Waldorf Salad

Serves 2 • **Prep** 20 mins

INGREDIENTS

Braeburn Apple – Cored and diced into bitesize chunks	1 Apple
Lemon Juice	1 Tbsp/15ml
Romaine Lettuce – Rinsed and drained	1 Heart/170g
Red Onion – Peeled and thinly sliced	½ Sm/50g
Celery – Thinly sliced	2 Stalks/80g
Walnuts - Chopped	6 Halves/20g
Mayonnaise	1 Tbsp/13g
Roast Chicken Breast – Skin removed	2 Small Breasts/200g
Black Pepper	1 Pinch

NUTRITION INFO per Serving

Cals	Protein	Carbs	Sugar	Fat	Sat Fat	Fibre	Fruit and Veg
311	27.9g	11.5g	8.4g	17.0g	2.4g	3g	2.8

METHOD

1. Put the apple pieces into a bowl. Stir in the lemon juice to coat the apples.

2. Add the onion, celery and walnuts to the apple. Stir in the mayonnaise.

3. Cut the chicken into bite sized cubes and mix with the other ingredients.

4. Line the serving dish with the lettuce leaves and pile the chicken salad into the centre.

5. Add a sprinkle of freshly ground black pepper to taste.

You can add a chunk of crusty bread for around an extra 100 calories.

A simple, substantial and scrumptious Spanish favourite that will easily help you to feel full until your next meal. Once mastered have a go experimenting with different ingredients to put in your tortilla.

Spanish Tortilla

Serves 2 • **Prep** 5 mins • **Cook** 15 mins

INGREDIENTS

Olive Oil	2 Tsp/10ml
Potatoes – Peeled and thinly sliced	200g
Onions – Peeled and sliced	½ Med/90g
Red Pepper – De-seeded and sliced into strips	1 Med/160g
Cherry Tomatoes - Halved	8 Tomatoes/120g
Large Eggs	4 Eggs
Salt	1 Pinch
Black Pepper	1 Pinch
Green Salad Leaves	200g
Fresh Parsley – Roughly chopped	½ Tbsp/2g
Olive Oil Spray	10 Sprays

NUTRITION INFO per Serving

Cals	Protein	Carbs	Sugar	Fat	Sat Fat	Fibre	Fruit and Veg
386	21g	28.4g	11g	21.1g	5.1g	4.3g	3.6

METHOD

1. Put a non stick frying pan over a high heat. Add the oil and heat through. Reduce the heat to medium and add the potatoes, onion and peppers and cook through, stirring regularly, for about 15 minutes until tender.

2. Add the cherry tomatoes to the pan - continue to cook the mixture for another 3 - 5 minutes. Take off the heat and drain through a sieve over a bowl to reserve any oil.

3. Beat the eggs in a large bowl and season with a generous pinch of both salt and pepper. Stir the vegetable mixture and the chopped parsley into the eggs.

4. Scrape the frying pan out of any remaining bits and re-heat over a medium to high heat with half of the reserved oil (If you need to add more oil use a little spray oil). Add the mixture into the pan and smooth down with a spatula or the back of a wooden spoon - pressing into an even layer. Cook for around 4 - 5 minutes, shaking the pan gently occasionally to ensure the tortilla doesn't stick.

5. Once the base is set place a large plate over the top of the pan and turn the tortilla out. Put the pan back on the heat with the remaining oil and carefully slide the tortilla back into the pan, cooked side up. Use the spatula/spoon to smooth the edges in. Continue to cook for 2 - 3 minutes until set and golden brown. Slide the tortilla onto a plate and leave to cool for a few minutes before slicing.

Serve with a side salad of greens. You could also serve this with a couple of slices of parma ham each for an extra 43kcal per person.

A really quick dish for those nights when you just want to get something on a plate but don't want to compromise on enjoyment. Easily double up the ingredients to cook for two.

Chicken with Creamy Garlic Mushrooms and Dressed Rocket Salad

Serves 1 • **Prep** 5 mins • **Cook** 15 mins

INGREDIENTS

Chicken Breast, Skinless and Boneless	1 Breast/120g
Large Flat Mushrooms	2 Mushrooms/105g
Soft Cheese	50g
Lemon Peel - Finely grated	1 Tsp
Garlic –Peeled and crushed	1 Clove
Salt	1 Pinch
Black Pepper	1 Pinch
Baby Spinach	25g
Water	2 Tbsp
Rocket	80g
Lemon Juice	½ Juiced Lemon
Dijon Mustard	¼ Tsp
Olive Oil	1 Tsp

NUTRITION INFO per Serving

Cals	Protein	Carbs	Sugar	Fat	Sat Fat	Fibre	Fruit and Veg
400	42.6g	4.4g	2.2g	23.6g	10.9g	2.6g	3.1

METHOD

1. Preheat the grill to a medium to high heat. Place the chicken breast under the grill and cook for 8-10 minutes per side, or until thoroughly cooked.

2. While the chicken breast cooks, put the water into a frying pan big enough for the mushrooms over a low heat. Add the mushrooms to the pan, gills upwards.

3. Mix the soft cheese with the lemon rind, a pinch each of salt and pepper and the crushed garlic. Fill the mushrooms and cook gently for 5-6 minutes.

4. Add the spinach to the mushroom pan and allow to wilt for 2 minutes.

5. To make a dressing for the rocket salad juice half the lemon and mix together with the dijon mustard, olive oil and a very small pinch each of salt and pepper. (You can do this really easily in a small jar by adding the ingredients and shaking well).

6. When the chicken is cooked through serve with the mushrooms and the spinach (be careful to drain both thoroughly before putting on the plate). Arrange the rocket on the plate and drizzle over the dressing.

Salmon is full of goodness and is a real nutritional win – make this quick and simple fresh fish dish one of your weekly oily fish portions.

Pan Fried Salmon
with Chilli & Lime

Serves 2 • **Prep** 5 mins • **Cook** 15 mins

INGREDIENTS

Salmon Fillets with Skin (Ready to Cook)	2 Sm Fillets/240g
Spring Onions – Finely sliced diagonally	3 Med/45g
Red Chilli Peppers – De-seeded and finely chopped	½ Med Pepper
Lime – Zested and juiced	½ Lime
Fresh Coriander Leaves – Finely chopped	10g
Basmati Rice	100g
Butter	20g
Olive Oil Spray	5 Sprays
Salt	1 Pinch

NUTRITION INFO per Serving

Cals	Protein	Carbs	Sugar	Fat	Sat Fat	Fibre	Fruit and Veg
493	30g	42.2g	0.9g	22.9g	8.3g	2.4g	0.7

METHOD

1. Bring a pan of salted water to the boil and cook the rice as per the packet instructions.

2. While the rice cooks, heat the oil in a large frying pan and cook the salmon, skin side down, for about 5-6 mins until the skin is crispy and golden. Turn the salmon fillets carefully, then cook for a further 2 mins. Remove from the pan and set aside.

3. Drain the rice and set aside.

4. Add the butter to the pan the salmon was cooked in and, when melted, add the spring onions, chilli and lime zest to cook for 2 minutes, then add the lime juice. Return the salmon fillets to the pan and spoon the chilli and lime infused butter over the salmon.

Serve the salmon along with the (fluffed up) rice, spooning any remaining sauce from the pan over the top. Scatter the chopped coriander on top.

A quick stir fry is probably one of the easiest and freshest meals you can make if you're short of time.

Really Easy Chinese Prawn Stir Fry with Noodles

Serves 1 • **Prep** 10 mins • **Cook** 10 mins

INGREDIENTS

Vegetable or Sunflower Oil	1 Tsp
Carrots – Peeled and finely sliced into strips	50g
Mange Tout	50g
Spring Onions – Finely sliced	50g
Five Spice Powder	¼ Tsp
Bean Sprouts	50g
Prawns, Cooked & Peeled	100g
Soy Sauce	4 Tsp/20ml
Straight To Wok Egg Noodles	1 Pouch/150g
Red Chilli Peppers – De-seeded and finely chopped	½ Sm Pepper/13g
Garlic – Peeled and Crushed	1 Clove

NUTRITION INFO per Serving

Cals	Protein	Carbs	Sugar	Fat	Sat Fat	Fibre	Fruit and Veg
438	31.1g	60g	7.8g	9.3g	1.2g	4.8g	2.7

METHOD

1. Heat the oil on a high heat in a wok or large frying pan and stir fry the carrots, spring onions and mange tout for 5 minutes.

2. Add the beansprouts, chilli, five spice powder and garlic and stir fry for a further 2 minutes.

3. Add the prawns and soy sauce, stir-fry for a further 3 minutes, then add the straight to wok noodles and continue to stir fry for another 2 minutes. You can add a couple of tablespoons of water at this point if you prefer a slightly thinner sauce/spice coating.

All in one pan, a few minutes cooking and there you have it – an easy, flavoursome meal in minutes.

A creamy pasta treat great for weeknights where speed and ease are needed.

Courgette and Ricotta Penne with Chicken

Serves 2 • **Prep** 5 mins • **Cook** 15 mins

INGREDIENTS

Penne, Dry	175g
Chicken Breast, Skinless and Boneless – Sliced into strips	1 Large Breast/150g
Courgette – Sliced into ½ cm rounds then cut in half	1 Courgette/224g
Olive Oil	1 Tsp
Ricotta Cheese	50g
Mushrooms – Peeled and sliced	60g
Garlic – Peeled and crushed	1 Clove
Lemon - Zested	½ Lemon
Fresh Basil – Finely chopped	1 Tbsp
Fresh Mint – Finely chopped	1 Tbsp
Salt	1 Pinch
Black Pepper	1 Pinch

NUTRITION INFO per Serving

Cals	Protein	Carbs	Sugar	Fat	Sat Fat	Fibre	Fruit and Veg
487	36.8g	66.1g	4.6g	8.5g	2.8g	4.1g	2

METHOD

1. Put a pan of slightly salted water on to boil. Add the penne and cook for 10-12 minutes (or as per pack instructions).

2. While the penne is cooking put a frying pan on a medium heat with the olive oil. Add the chicken strips to the pan and cook through (about 5 minutes).

3. Add the garlic, courgette and mushrooms and saute until the courgette is cooked through but still has some bite (about 5 minutes). Season to taste with a pinch of salt and pepper. Take the pan off the heat and add the lemon zest and the ricotta and stir through. Stir in the basil and mint.

4. Drain the penne. You can either mix the penne through with the chicken and ricotta mixture, or serve the penne on plates, spooning the sauce over the top.

This is the sort of dish you'd see on an Italian restaurant menu. Good to cook if you've got company... the rich cream sauce really feels like a treat!

Chicken in a Brandy Cream Sauce with Asparagus

Serves 1 • **Prep** 5 mins • **Cook** 20 mins

INGREDIENTS

New Potatoes – Washed and cut into halves	150g
Salt	1 Pinch
Black Pepper	1 Pinch
Olive Oil	2 Tsp/10ml
Garlic – Peeled and thinly sliced	½ Clove
Brandy	1 Tbsp/15ml
Single Cream	1 Tbsp/15ml
Chicken Breast, Skinless and Boneless	1 Breast/120g
Onion – Peeled and finely chopped	½ Sm Onion/50g
Asparagus – Trimmed	100g

NUTRITION INFO per Serving

Cals	Protein	Carbs	Sugar	Fat	Sat Fat	Fibre	Fruit and Veg
454	39.7g	32g	6.5g	15.6g	3.7g	4.8g	2

METHOD

1. Preheat the grill to a medium high heat. Put two saucepans of salted water on to boil.

2. Put the potatoes in one of the pans of water to boil until tender (usually around 10-15 minutes).

3. Brush the chicken all over with one teaspoon of olive oil, then season generously with salt and pepper. Place the chicken on foil under the grill and cook for 8-10 minutes each side, or until thoroughly cooked.

4. While the chicken is cooking heat the remaining oil in a frying pan and add the onions and garlic and saute for 3-4 minutes. Add the brandy to the pan and turn the heat up to burn off the alcohol. After a minute or two, take the pan off the heat and stir the cream through. Put the pan on a low heat and bring the mixture to a gentle simmer. Adjust the consistency of the sauce using a little water if necessary. Allow to simmer and thicken for 4-5 minutes.

5. Add the asparagus to the remaining pan of boiling water and simmer for about 5 minutes, until tender but still with a little bite.

6. Drain the potatoes and asparagus, and serve with chicken, pouring the creamy sauce over the chicken.

If you like chicken satay then you'll love this dish... a taste of a Chinese takeaway without breaking the calorie bank.

Chicken in Spicy Peanut Sauce

Serves 1 • **Prep** 5 mins • **Cook** 20 mins

INGREDIENTS

Carrots – Peeled and sliced into thin batons	½ Carrot/40g
Sunflower Oil	1 Tsp/5ml
Chicken Breast, Skinless and Boneless – Sliced into strips	1 Small Breast/100g
Cous Cous	1 Serving/50g
Garlic – Peeled and crushed	½ Clove
Red Chilli Peppers – De-seeded and finely chopped	½ Sm Pepper
Ground Cumin	¼ Tsp
Smooth Peanut Butter	1 Tbsp/15g
Salt	1 Pinch
Black Pepper	1 Pinch
Lemon Juice	1 Tsp/5ml

NUTRITION INFO per Serving

Cals	Protein	Carbs	Sugar	Fat	Sat Fat	Fibre	Fruit and Veg
464	38.7g	42.2g	4.9g	16g	3g	3.1g	0.6

METHOD

1. Set a pan (preferably a wok) over a medium heat with the sunflower oil. Toss is the sliced carrots and stir fry. Add the sliced chicken breast to the pan and cook through, stirring continuously, for 6-8 minutes or until the chicken is cooked through.

2. Add the garlic, chilli, peanut butter, cumin and a splash of boiling water to a food processor. Season with salt and pepper and blitz until almost fine, adding more water if necessary to get a thick sauce. (If you don't have a food processor then mix thoroughly with a fork).

3. Prepare the cous cous as per the packet instructions.

4. Meanwhile set a frying pan over a medium heat and cook the peanut mixture until simmering. Turn down the heat slightly and simmer for a few minutes, stirring to ensure it doesn't catch on the bottom of the pan.

5. Remove the sauce from the heat and stir in the lemon juice. Add the peanut sauce to the chicken breast and carrot and cook for a further 2 minutes before serving with the cous cous.

Sometimes only steak will do! This rich, creamy, indulgent meal for one can easily double up to cook for two.

Steak in a Creamy Mushroom and Brandy Sauce with New Potatoes

Serves 1 • **Prep** 5 mins • **Cook** 20 mins

INGREDIENTS

Baby New Potatoes	150g
Salt	1 Pinch
Black Pepper	1 Pinch
Olive Oil	2 Tsp
Mushrooms – Peeled and sliced	70g
Garlic – Peeled and thinly sliced	½ Clove
Sirloin Steak – Visible fat removed	1 Steak/150g
Fine Green Beans	100g
Brandy	1 Tbsp
Single Cream	1 Tbsp

NUTRITION INFO per Serving

Cals	Protein	Carbs	Sugar	Fat	Sat Fat	Fibre	Fruit and Veg
493	41.3g	29.9g	4.5g	20g	6.1g	6.1g	2.3

METHOD

1. Place a griddle or frying pan over a medium to high heat and put two saucepans of salted water on to boil.

2. Put the potatoes in one of the pans of water to boil until tender (usually around 10-15 minutes).

3. Brush the steak all over with one teaspoon of olive oil, then season generously with salt and pepper. Lay the steak in the hot griddle pan and cook, turning every minute or so until cooked to your liking (about 4-10 minutes depending on how you like it cooked). Once cooked set aside to rest.

4. Put the green beans into the second pan of water and simmer for 5-7 minutes until tender.

5. While the beans are cooking heat the remaining oil in the pan the steak was cooked in. Add the mushrooms and garlic and saute for 2-3 minutes. Add the brandy to the pan and turn the heat up to burn off the alcohol. After a minute or two turn the heat down to low and stir the cream through bringing the mixture to a gentle simmer. Adjust the consistency of the sauce using some of the water from the green beans if necessary.

6. Drain the potatoes and beans, and serve with steak, pouring the creamy sauce over the steak.

Something a bit different, this is really easy to make and fantastic if you're a big Chorizo fan!

Italian Style Pan-Fried Pork
with Chorizo

Serves 2 • **Prep** 10 mins • **Cook** 15 mins

INGREDIENTS

Chorizo Sausage – Sliced	50g
Olive Oil	2 Tsp
Garlic – Peeled and finely sliced	1½ Cloves
Red Onion – Peeled and finely sliced	1 Sm/90g
Red Pepper – De-seeded and thinly sliced	½ Pepper
Paprika	1 Tsp
Chopped Tomatoes, Canned	½ Can/200g
Black Pepper	1 Pinch
Salt	1 Pinch
White Rice	100g
Pork Tenderloin Steak – Visible fat removed and cut into strips	200g
Fresh Basil – Roughly chopped	1 Tbsp

NUTRITION INFO per Serving

Cals	Protein	Carbs	Sugar	Fat	Sat Fat	Fibre	Fruit and Veg
463	32.1g	50.1g	7.4g	14.5g	1.4g	2.4g	2.4

METHOD

1. Put a pan of slightly salted water on to boil for the rice. Add the rice to the pan and cook for about 12 minutes (or as per the pack instructions).

2. While the rice is cooking heat the oil in a large frying pan over a medium heat. Add the onion, pepper and garlic to the pan and saute gently until softened (about 3 minutes).

3. Add the pork and chorizo to the pan and continue to cook for about 5 - 7 minutes or until the pork is just cooked through.

4. Add the paprika and a pinch of black pepper and stir well. Add the tomatoes to the pan and season with a pinch of salt to taste. Bring to a simmer, cover and cook for 10 minutes.

5. Once the rice is cooked drain and set aside for a couple of minutes before serving.

To serve fluff through the rice with a fork and spoon the pork on top. Sprinkle with some torn basil leaves.

A real classic – great for summer lunches or light suppers. If you don't have spray oil you can always use regular olive oil and use a (well rinsed) pump action bottle.

Chicken Caesar Salad

Serves 1 • **Prep** 10 mins • **Cook** 20 mins

INGREDIENTS

Black Pepper	1 Pinch
Little Gem Lettuce	1 Heart/90g
Garlic – Peeled and crushed	½ Clove
Anchovy Fillets – Finely chopped	½ Anchovy
Greek Yoghurt, 0% Fat	1 Tbsp/15ml
Lemon Juice	1 Tsp/5ml
Parmesan Cheese	25g
Chicken Breast, Skinless and Boneless	1 Breast/120g
Olive Oil Spray	5 Pumps
Salt	1 Pinch

NUTRITION INFO per Serving

Cals	Protein	Carbs	Sugar	Fat	Sat Fat	Fibre	Fruit and Veg
293	45.7g	2.6g	2.2g	11.2g	5.9g	0.4g	1.3

METHOD

1. Heat a griddle or frying pan on a medium heat, spritz the chicken breast with a little olive oil and season with salt and pepper.

2. Place onto the pan, cook for 5 minutes then turn over and repeat for further 5 minutes, or until cooked through. Remove from heat and leave to rest for 5 mins, then cut into 1cm slices widthways.

3. Place the crushed garlic, anchovy and some salt and pepper into a pestle and mortar and pound until broken into a smooth paste (if you don't have a pestle and mortar you can do this in a bowl with the back of a spoon). Tablespoon by tablespoon, add the yoghurt and lemon juice until combined. Season to your liking with salt and pepper.

4. Slice off the very bottom of the little gem and separate the lettuce leaves. Rinse with cold water and drain. Mix the dressing with the lettuce leaves. Place on plate and top with sliced cooked chicken. Grate or shave the parmesan on top.

Add a chunk of crusty or ciabbata bread for around 100-150 extra calories.

Shredded Chilli Beef
with Rice

Serves 2 • **Prep** 15 mins • **Cook** 15 mins

INGREDIENTS

Sirloin Steak – Visible fat removed and sliced into thin strips	200g
Carrots – Peeled and thinly sliced	100g
Spring Onions – thinly sliced into strips	2 Onions/30g
Caster Sugar	2 Tsp/10g
Chicken Stock Cubes	1 Cube
Cornflour	½ Tsp/2.5g
Water	50ml
Soy Sauce	1 Tbsp/15ml
Salt	A Pinch
Plain Flour	1 Tbsp/15g
Vegetable or Sunflower Oil	1 Tbsp/15ml
Garlic– Finely sliced	1 Clove
Red Chilli Pepper – De-seeded and finely chopped	1 Med/45g
Rice Vinegar	4 Tsp/20ml

NUTRITION INFO per Serving

Cals	Protein	Carbs	Sugar	Fat	Sat Fat	Fibre	Fruit and Veg
301	25.9g	22.2g	11.6g	12.3g	2.7g	1.8g	1.1

METHOD

1. Heat oil in a wok or large frying pan until smoking. Make up the stock cube with 50ml boiling water.

2. Place flour and salt into a bag with the steak strips and toss to cover. Stir-fry steak for 4-5mins until steak is crispy, then remove steak with slotted spoon and rest on sheets of kitchen roll.

3. Stir-fry carrots for 1 minute then add onions, garlic and chillies stir-fry for another minute. Add the sugar, vinegar, soy sauce and stock. Bring to the boil.

4. Blend the corn flour with 1 Tbsp water then add to vegetable mix and stir well, simmer until thickened. Add the steak back into the pan and stir through to cover with the sauce.

Serve with 50g rice or egg noodles per person for an extra 175 calories (making a total meal for 476 calories).

A quick and simple meal for one (easily double up the ingredients to cook for two). This is great for summer evenings and gives you over 3 of your daily portions of fruit and veg.

Asian Style Sea Bass with Rice

Serves 1 • **Prep** 5 mins • **Cook** 25 mins

INGREDIENTS

Sea Bass Fillet (Ready to cook)	1 Fillet/95g
Salt	1 Pinch
Black Pepper	1 Pinch
Basmati Rice	50g
Fresh Ginger – Peeled and finely chopped	1 Tsp
Garlic – Peeled and crushed	1 Clove
Lemon Grass – Chopped	¼ Stalk
Fresh Coriander – Finely chopped	½ Tbsp
Red Chilli Pepper – De-seeded and finely chopped	½ Sm Pepper/13g
Spring Onion – Finely sliced	1 Onion/15g
Soy Sauce	1 Tbsp/15ml
Fish Sauce	½ Tsp
Sesame Oil	1 Tsp/5ml
Lime Juice	3 Tsp/15ml
Mange Tout	100g
Baby Corn	100g

NUTRITION INFO per Serving

Cals	Protein	Carbs	Sugar	Fat	Sat Fat	Fibre	Fruit and Veg
415	31g	51.4g	8.3g	9.7g	1.7g	3.9g	3.2

METHOD

1. Preheat the oven to 180C/350F/Gas Mark 4. Put a pan of water on the hob to boil ready to cook the rice.

2. Season the sea bass with salt and pepper and lay in a high sided tray and cover tightly with 2 layers of foil. Place in the oven for 15-20 minutes.

3. While the sea bass cooks , cook the rice as per the packet instructions. Set another saucepan of water to boil over a high heat for the mange tout and baby corn.

4. To make the dressing, add the ginger, garlic and lemon grass to a food processor with the coriander, red chilli, spring onion, soy sauce, fish sauce, ½ tsp of the sesame oil and 2tsp of the lime juice. Process until finely chopped and pour into a bowl.

5. Add the mange tout and baby corn to the pan of boiling water and cook for about 3-4 minutes, drain and toss through with the remainder of the sesame oil and lime juice.

6. Uncover the sea bass, spoon over the juices and serve with the dressing drizzled on top next to the fluffed rice and the Asian vegetables.

Butternut Squash Risotto

Serves 2 • **Prep** 5 mins • **Cook** 25 mins

INGREDIENTS

Olive Oil	1 Tbsp/15ml
Onions - Finely chopped	1 Sm Onion/90g
Butternut Squash – Peeled, de-seeded and cut into 1 cm cubes	150g
Risotto Rice	100g
Fresh Oregano – Finely chopped	1 Tsp
Black Pepper	1 Pinch
Parmesan Cheese - Grated	1 Tbsp
Vegetable Stock Cube	1 Cube
Salt	1 Pinch
Single Cream	1 Tbsp

NUTRITION INFO per Serving

Cals	Protein	Carbs	Sugar	Fat	Sat Fat	Fibre	Fruit and Veg
323	9.3g	47.9g	6g	10.6g	1.7g	2.8g	1.4

METHOD

1. Put a large frying/sauté pan on the hob on a medium heat. Fry the onion in the olive oil for 2-3 minutes until soft. Make up the stock cube with boiling water to 1 pint.

2. Add the squash and rice to the pan and stir until the grains are coated with oil. Add 2 ladles of stock and the oregano and bring to a simmer.

3. Turn the hob down to a low heat and cook, stirring until almost all the stock is absorbed.

4. Add the rest of the stock a little at a time, cooking until each addition is absorbed, the squash is soft and the rice is al dente and creamy. Season well with salt and pepper.

5. Once served into bowls add a swirl of cream to serve (about ½ Tbsp per person) and scatter with parmesan.

Sometimes you just can't beat a good bit of steak!

Fillet Steak in a Redcurrant Sauce with Dijon Mash

Serves 1 • **Prep** 10 mins • **Cook** 20 mins

INGREDIENTS

Beef Fillet Steak – Visible Fat Removed	140g
Potatoes – Peeled and cut into large, similar sized chunks for mashing	200g
Creme Fraiche, Reduced Fat	1 Tbsp/15ml
Red Wine	25ml
Vegetable Stock Cube	¼ Cube
Balsamic Vinegar	1 Tbsp/15ml
Garlic – Peeled and crushed	½ Clove
Fresh Thyme – Finely chopped	1 Tsp
Dijon Mustard	1 Tsp
Savoy Cabbage – Shredded	1 Serving/90g
Redcurrant Sauce	1 Heaped Tsp
Salt	1 Pinch
Black Pepper	1 Pinch

NUTRITION INFO per Serving

Cals	Protein	Carbs	Sugar	Fat	Sat Fat	Fibre	Fruit and Veg
500	36.4g	54.5g	5.6g	14.1g	6.6g	5.5g	1.2

METHOD

1. Season the steak with salt and pepper and place it in a bowl with the balsamic vinegar, the garlic and the thyme. Rub the mixture all over the steak and set aside to marinate. (The longer you can allow the steak to marinate the better, but at least 10 minutes works fine).

2. Put the potatoes in a saucepan of cold water with a pinch of salt and bring to the boil. Cook through ready for mashing (usually about 15 minutes or until you can easily slide a knife in).

3. Heat a griddle or frying pan over a medium heat. Add the steak and its marinade and fry for 2-3 mins each side for medium, depending on the thickness of the steak. Remove the steak from the pan and set aside to rest (Leaving the juices/marinade in the pan).

4. Put the cabbage in a pan and add boiling water to about 2 thirds of the height of the cabbage. Simmer (stirring once or twice) for about 5 minutes or until tender. Make up the stock cube with 100ml of boiling water.

5. While the cabbage is cooking add the red wine and vegetable stock to the steak pan and stir, scraping the bottom of the pan to de-glaze it and put flavour into the sauce. Simmer for a couple of minutes then stir in the redcurrant sauce and allow to simmer for another couple of minutes.

6. Drain the potato and mash with the creme fraiche and dijon mustard. Season with salt and pepper to your liking.

Serve the steak on a plate with the mash and cabbage, drizzle the sauce over the steak.

Stuffed Chicken Breast

Serves 1 • **Prep** 10 mins • **Cook** 25 mins

INGREDIENTS

Onions – Finely chopped	50g
Lean Back Bacon – Diced into small pieces	2 Rasher/66g
Black Pepper	1 Pinch/0.2g
Olive Oil Spray	5 Sprays/1ml
Small Chicken Breast, Skinless and Boneless	1 Breast/100g
Mushrooms – Cleaned, peeled and roughly chopped	1 Handfull/30g
Garlic – Peeled and crushed	1 Clove/3g
Dried Mixed Herbs	¼ Tsp/1g
Low Fat Soft Cheese	1 Tbsp/30g
Fine Green Beans	100g

NUTRITION INFO per Serving

Cals	Protein	Carbs	Sugar	Fat	Sat Fat	Fibre	Fruit and Veg
340	45.3g	9.7g	6.2g	13.3g	1.9g	4.5g	2.4

METHOD

1. Slice into the chicken breast to make a pocket and place on foil on an oven proof tray.

2. Pre-heat oven to 180C/350F/Gas Mark 4.

3. Warm the spray oil in a frying pan and gently fry off the bacon, onion and garlic until coloured. Lower the heat and add the mushrooms, pepper and dried mixed herbs. Mix and ensure all heated through until the mushrooms have started to colour or shrink slightly.

4. Spoon the mixture into the pocket in the chicken breast along with the soft cheese. If there's any of the mixture left put it on the top.

5. Wrap the foil around chicken breast and cook in the oven for 20-30 minutes (until thoroughly cooked).

6. When the chicken has about 10 minutes left to cook, steam or boil the fine green beans for 5-7 minutes until tender.

Serve the chicken with the green beans. For an extra 100 calories you could add 150g of boiled new potatoes.

Pan Fried Pork
with Maple & Mustard Sauce
Serves 2 • **Prep** 10 mins • **Cook** 25 mins

INGREDIENTS

Pork Tenderloin Fillets – Visible fat removed	2 Sm Fillets/300g
Plain Flour	10g
Olive Oil	1 Tsp
Red Onions – Peeled and finely sliced	1 Med/180g
Maple Syrup	1 Tbsp
Whole Grain Mustard	1 Tbsp
Lemon - Juiced	½ Juiced Lemon
Vegetable Stock Cube	1 Cube
Baby New Potatoes	300g
Water	100ml
Salt	1 Pinch
Black Pepper	1 Pinch

NUTRITION INFO per Serving

Cals	Protein	Carbs	Sugar	Fat	Sat Fat	Fibre	Fruit and Veg
499	53.4g	44g	13.2g	12.8g	2.2g	4.2g	1.3

METHOD

1. Put the potatoes in a pan of cold water with a pinch of salt and bring to the boil. Cook for 15-20 minutes until tender. Make the stock cube up with 100ml of boiling water.

2. Meanwhile, mix the flour with a pinch of salt and pepper and lightly coat the pork with flour. Heat the oil in a large pan and cook the pork for about 8-10 minutes on each side until lightly browned and thoroughly cooked. Set the pork aside leaving the juices in the pan.

3. In the same pan, fry the sliced onion until translucent. Add the stock and boil hard for a couple of minutes to reduce. Add the maple syrup, mustard and lemon juice, stir thoroughly and heat through.

4. Return the pork to the pan, mix with the sauce, and simmer for a few minutes until completely heated through. Drain the potatoes.

Serve the pork with the new potatoes, spooning the sauce on top. You could also add some steamed veg such as fine green beans or cauliflower.

This stew (or broth) is quick and easy to make and great for warmer days. It packs a real flavour punch and is filled with goodness.

Sicilian-Style Fish Stew
with Ciabbatta Breadsticks

Serves 2 • **Prep** 15 mins • **Cook** 20 mins

INGREDIENTS

Garlic – Peeled and crushed	2 Cloves
Celery – Thickly sliced	2 Sticks/80g
Tomatoes – Roughly chopped	2 Large/360g
Cous Cous	50g
White Wine	125ml
Lemon - Zested	½ Lemon
Fresh Parsley – Finely chopped	1 Tbsp
Water	500ml
Vegetable Stock Cubes	1 Cube
Fish Stock Cubes	1 Cube
Monkfish Fillets (Ready to Cook)	300g
King Prawns (Ready to Cook)	100g
Ciabatta Roll	1 Sm Roll/80g
Olive Oil	2 Tsp
Chilli Flakes	½ Tsp
Onions – Peeled and roughly chopped	1 Sm Onion/90g
Salt	1 Pinch
Black Pepper	1 Pinch

METHOD

1. Put the grill on to a medium heat. Heat 1 tsp of the olive oil in a wide, shallow pan on a medium heat. Add the onion, celery, garlic, chilli flakes and a pinch of salt and pepper. Cook for 5-10 minutes, stirring frequently to make sure it doesn't catch on the bottom of the pan.

2. Crumble both stock cubes into a jug and make up with 500ml boiling water. Cut the ciabatta roll in half (as if to make a sandwich), then cut each half into strips about 1cm thick. Brush the bread strips with the remaining olive oil.

3. Add the tomatoes to the pan and cook for another couple of minutes. Pour in the wine and stock and bring to the boil. Cook for a few minutes then add the couscous. Turn down to a simmer and add the monk fish and prawns. Cover with a lid and cook until the fish is done, about 7-10 minutes.

4. Just before you are ready to serve your stew place the ciabatta fingers under the grill to toast for 2-3 minutes until golden brown and crispy.

5. Divide the stew between 2 dishes, breaking the fish into large pieces. Sprinkle over the lemon zest and parsley to finish and serve the breadsticks on the side.

NUTRITION INFO per Serving

Cals	Protein	Carbs	Sugar	Fat	Sat Fat	Fibre	Fruit and Veg
500	43.4g	52.1g	10.3g	10g	2.2g	6.3g	3.9

*A classic American/Italian dish, this is ultra comfort food –
and it contains three and half of your five a day!*

Chicken Parmigiana
with Potato Wedges

Serves 2 • **Prep** 10 mins • **Cook** 30 mins

INGREDIENTS

Chicken Breast, Skinless and Boneless	2 Small Breasts/200g
Medium Egg	1 Egg
Breadcrumbs	25g
Parmesan Cheese, Grated	25g
Olive Oil	1 Tsp
Garlic – Peeled and crushed	1 Clove
Passata	325g
Caster Sugar	½ Tsp
Dried Oregano	½ Tsp
Mozzarella Cheese	30g
Maris Piper Potatoes – Washed and cut into segments	300g
Sunflower Oil Spray	10 Sprays
Black Pepper	1 Pinch
Salt	1 Pinch
Green Salad Leaves	200g

NUTRITION INFO per Serving

Cals	Protein	Carbs	Sugar	Fat	Sat Fat	Fibre	Fruit and Veg
499	44.3g	48g	10.4g	14g	3.7g	5.2g	3.5

METHOD

1. Preheat the oven to 200C/400F/Gas Mark 6 and place a roasting tin into the oven to heat.

2. Par boil the potato wedges in a pan of salted boiling water for 5-10 minutes (or until you can just poke a knife into them). Then drain and leave aside for now.

3. Beat the egg, grate the parmesan and tear the mozzarella into small pieces.

4. Place the chicken breasts between cling film sheets and flatten with a rolling pin until they are about the thickness of your finger. Dip them in the egg, then in the breadcrumbs mixed with half the Parmesan.

5. Put the potato wedges in a bowl and spray with sunflower oil. Sprinkle over some salt and pepper and mix thoroughly to coat. Tip them into the roasting tray you've had heating in the oven to cook for 20-30 minutes (or until golden brown).

6. Heat the olive oil in a pan and fry the chicken briskly for about 3 minutes on each side until golden brown. Remove from the pan, put in a shallow ovenproof dish and continue cooking in oven for 10 minutes or until cooked through.

7. Meanwhile put the crushed garlic into the pan previously used for chicken and fry gently for 1 min, then tip in passata, sugar and oregano. Season and simmer for 10 mins.

8. Remove the chicken from the oven, lift it out of the dish and set aside. Pour the tomato sauce into the ovenproof dish, and place the chicken on top. Sprinkle the mozzarella and remaining Parmesan on top and return to the oven for 3-4 mins until the cheese has melted. Serve the chicken with your homemade healthy wedges and some green salad leaves.

If you're looking for something fresh and filling for less than 400 calories you can't go wrong with this beautiful Italian fish dish.

Haddock Baked in Italian Tomato and Olive Sauce

Serves 1 • **Prep** 5 mins • **Cook** 35 mins

INGREDIENTS

Chopped Tomatoes, Canned	½ Can/200g
Black Olives, Pitted - Sliced	8 Olives/28g
Garlic – Peeled and crushed	1 Clove
Sugar	½ Tsp
Salt	1 Pinch
Black Pepper	1 Pinch
Haddock Fillet (Ready to cook)	1 Fillet/140g
Sunflower Oil Spray	10 Sprays
Fresh Basil - Finely chopped	1 Tbsp
Rice (White or Basmati)	50g

NUTRITION INFO per Serving

Cals	Protein	Carbs	Sugar	Fat	Sat Fat	Fibre	Fruit and Veg
397	31.7g	50.3g	7.4g	7.8g	1.2g	3.2g	3.1

METHOD

1. Preheat the oven to 200C/400F/Gas Mark 6.

2. Add the chopped tomatoes, olives, garlic and sugar to an ovenproof (casserole style) dish and cook, covered, in the oven for 15-20 minutes. (If you don't have a lid you can cover the dish with foil).

3. While the sauce is cooking set a frying pan over a high heat with the oil. Season the fish with salt and pepper and add to the pan. Cook for 3-4 minutes each side (turning once) until cooked through.

4. Set a pan of lightly salted water on to boil ready to cook the rice. Add the rice and allow to simmer on a medium heat for around 12 minutes (or as per pack instructions).

5. Add the haddock to the casserole dish with the tomato sauce making sure it is well covered by the sauce. Cover and return to the oven to cook for 10 minutes.

6. Once the rice is cooked, drain and allow to stand for a couple of minutes before serving.

7. Remove the haddock from the oven. Fluff the rice and serve with the baked haddock, sprinkled with the fresh basil.

A fantastic alternative to a greasy take away portion of fish and chips with fresh, zingy flavours for less than 500 calories.

Lime Crusted Fish
With Roast Potato Chips

Serves 2 • **Prep** 10 mins • **Cook** 30 mins

INGREDIENTS

Baby New Potatoes – Cut into small bite sized chunks	400g
Plaice Fillets (Ready to Cook)	300g
Olive Oil	2 Tbsp/30ml
Ciabatta Bread	30g
Fresh Parsley – Finely chopped	2 Tbsp
Fine Green Beans	200g
Tartare Sauce	2 Tsp
Lime	1 Lime/67g

NUTRITION INFO per Serving

Cals	Protein	Carbs	Sugar	Fat	Sat Fat	Fibre	Fruit and Veg
491	34.3g	47.8g	5.8g	19.1g	3.1g	7.5g	1.8

METHOD

1. Preheat oven to 220°C/435°F/Gas Mark 7. Place a roasting tin into the oven to heat up. Zest then juice the lime.

2. Place the ciabatta into a blender and pulse to form breadcrumbs.

3. Mix the breadcrumbs, lime zest and half of the lime juice with the chopped parsley.

4. Place the fish on a lightly greased baking tray and pour the remaining lime juice over the fish. Put the potato chunks and olive oil in a bowl or dish and mix the 'chips' until they are coated.

5. Leaving any excess oil in the bowl, put the chips into the now hot roasting tin and return the roasting tin along with the fish to the oven to cook for 10 minutes.

6. Remove the fish from the oven and carefully press the breadcrumb mixture onto the fish to form a crust. Turn the chips in the roasting tin over and return both to the oven for a further 15 to 20 minutes or until cooked. (Your fish may need to come out earlier than your potatoes – keep an eye on it so the crust doesn't burn).

7. While the fish and the potatoes finish cooking boil or steam the green beans as per the pack instructions (usually for around 5-8 minutes).

Serve the fish with the potatoes and green beans, and a dollop of tartare sauce.

This recipe is from WLR's founder – packed with veg, easy to prepare and with the taste of Mexico you can't go wrong.

Mexican Chicken
with Rice & Raita

Serves 2 • **Prep** 20 mins • **Cook** 20 mins

INGREDIENTS

Cornflour	½ Tsp
Chilli Powder	1 Tsp
Paprika	½ Tsp
Soft Brown Sugar	½ Tsp
Onion Powder (Leave out if you can't find this)	¼ Tsp
Ground Cumin	¼ Tsp
Garlic Salt	½ Tsp
Chicken Stock Cubes	1 Cube
Fat Free Greek Yoghurt	150g
Chicken Breast, Skinless and Boneless – Cut into strips	150g
Dried Mint	1 Tsp
Red Pepper – De-seeded and cut into bite size pieces	1 Med/160g
Green pepper – De-seeded and cut into bite size pieces	1 Med/160g
Red Onion – Peeled and cut into quarters, layers separated	1 Sm/90g
Cucumber – Peeled and cut into small cubes	100g
Frozen Peas and Sweetcorn	60g
Olive Oil	2 Tsp
Olive Oil Spray	10 Sprays
Basmati Rice (Microwave Pouch)	1 Pack/125g

METHOD

1. Add the cornflower, chilli powder, paprika, brown sugar, onion powder, cumin and garlic salt to a bowl, then crumble in half of the stock cube and mix well together. Add 25g of the yoghurt and mix well until you have a smooth paste.

2. Add the chicken to the bowl with the spice paste and mix well so that all the pieces of chicken are coated. Set aside while you prepare the vegetables. (You can leave the chicken to marinade in the paste in the fridge for a while if you have time.)

3. Stir the mint into the remaining yoghurt. Put the peas and sweetcorn in a pan and cover with boiling water, set aside.

4. Spray a non-stick frying pan with half the oil and put over a gentle heat. Add the chicken to the pan a piece at a time, reserve the paste left in the bowl. Keeping the heat gentle, fry the chicken, stirring frequently, for 10 minutes.

5. Once the chicken is on the go, spray a wok, or deep non-stick frying pan with the remaining oil and add one teaspoon of the olive oil. Put the pan on a low to medium heat and add the peppers and onions. Stir frequently.

6. After the chicken has been cooking for 10 minutes, tip it into the wok with the peppers and onions along with the residue of spice paste. Turn down the heat to very low, and stir frequently whilst you are preparing the rice.

7. Put the pan with the sweetcorn and peas on to boil and simmer for about 3 minutes. In the meantime, snip the bag and heat the rice in the microwave for 1 and a half minutes (as per the pack instructions).

8. Stir the cucumber into the minted yoghurt and put into one or two small serving bowls.

9. Put the chicken and peppers onto warm plates, and add 1 Tsp of olive oil to the empty wok. Add the rice and drained peas and sweetcorn to the wok and sprinkle with the remaining half stock cube. Stir fry over a high heat for 1 minute.

Portion the rice onto the plates with the chicken and serve with the cucumber raita.

NUTRITION INFO per Serving

Cals	Protein	Carbs	Sugar	Fat	Sat Fat	Fibre	Fruit and Veg
488	31g	63.2g	13.9g	12.4g	2g	6.8	3.4

weightlossresources.co.uk

Fad Free Tools for Healthy Weight Loss.

Take the Next Step with Weight Loss Resources - If you've enjoyed using our recipes then we think you'll enjoy our website

Who are Weight Loss Resources ?

We're an online calorie counting website – but before you throw up your hands in despair, we do all the hard work for you! Weight Loss Resources provides fad free tools for healthy weight loss. Working out what your body needs to reach you goals and making it easy to keep track of your food and activity. We give you the knowledge; tools and support you need to lose weight and keep it off.

How Does Weight Loss Resources Work?

You enter what you've eaten into your online food diary (you can even use your mobile), to track your calories, fat, protein and carbs, even your fruit & veg portions, water and salt intake. The programme does all the calculations for you to help you balance your calories.

You can calorie count your own recipes and search our online database of thousands of recipes.

If you need any support or help along the way, we have a nutritionally trained Helpteam on hand, and our members are a fantastic source of advice and support on the message boards – it's a really vibrant community.

Why Should You Use Weight Loss Resources?

We've helped thousands of people like you lose weight and keep it off, plus all of our staff are committed to helping you every step of the way – they use the tools themselves so know that it works from personal experience.

We have the most reliable food database in the UK with full nutrition information, and heaps of tips and advice from Dietitians and exercise professionals. We give you the bottom line about food and weight so you can go away with the knowledge you need to stay slim and healthy for life.

And, You Can Try it For Free

Go to **www.weightlossresources.co.uk** and take a free 24 hour trial of the tools – there's absolutely no obligation and we won't ask for any credit card details. Browse through our thousands of recipes, have a look at our great articles, (written by the UK's leading dietitians), share our members' success stories, and enjoy the latest updates from our resident weight loss blogger.

Fresh, zesty, zingy and delicious this is great for warmer weather and makes a change from using chicken.

Duck with Mango Salsa
and Noodles

Serves 2 • **Prep** 10 mins • **Cook** 30 mins

INGREDIENTS

Duck Breasts	2 Breasts/320g
Salt	1 Pinch
Black Pepper	1 Pinch
Red Onion – Peeled and finely chopped	½ Small/45g
Mango – Peeled and diced into small cubes	1 Mango
Lime – Juiced and zested	½ Lime
Red Chilli Pepper – De-seeded and finely chopped	1 Sm Pepper/13g
Sugar	1 Tsp
Fresh Mint – Finely chopped	1 Tbsp
Salt	¼ Tsp
Black Pepper	¼ Tsp
Straight to Wok Rice Noodles	2 Servings/240g
Sunflower or Vegetable Oil	1 Tsp

NUTRITION INFO per Serving

Cals	Protein	Carbs	Sugar	Fat	Sat Fat	Fibre	Fruit and Veg
416	39.2g	45g	16g	10.4g	2.4g	4.5g	1.9

METHOD

1. Mix together the red onion, mango, lime juice and zest, chilli, sugar, mint and a pinch of salt and pepper to make the salsa. Allow this to sit in a bowl while cooking the duck and potatoes to develop the flavours.

2. Trim as much fat from the edges of the duck breasts as possible. Season on the skin side with salt and pepper and lay skin side down in a frying pan. Then put the frying pan onto the hob on a medium heat. When the skin is just starting to go a little crispy (about 10 minutes) turn the duck over and cook for about 5-7 minutes or until cooked to your liking. Allow to rest.

3. Prepare the noodles as per the pack instructions in a wok or large frying pan with a teaspoon of sunflower oil.

4. To serve, remove the skin from the duck then slice diagonally. Arrange on a plate next to the noodles and spoon the salsa over the duck breast.

Who would have thought you could have a full on melting cheeseburger with chips for less than 500 calories?! These burgers are also great cooked on the BBQ, and you can experiment with putting different herbs and spices into the burger mixture – a WLR favourite is chopped fresh chilli.

Indulgent Cheeseburger
and Homemade Chips

Serves 2 • **Prep** 5 mins • **Cook** 35 mins

INGREDIENTS

Beef Mince, Extra Lean	200g
Shallots – Peeled and finely chopped	1 Shallot/50g
Worcestershire Sauce	1 Tsp
Garlic – Peeled and crushed	1 Clove
Small Soft White Bread Rolls	2 Rolls/90g
Tomatoes - Sliced	½ Medium/62g
Iceberg Lettuce	160g
Potatoes – Peeled and cut into chips or wedges	300g
Sunflower Oil Spray	20 Sprays
Mozzarella Cheese – Thinly sliced or grated	40g
Sunflower Oil	1 Tsp
Tomato Ketchup	4 Tsp
Red Onions	1 Sm/90g
Salt	1 Pinch
Black Pepper	1 Pinch

NUTRITION INFO per Serving

Cals	Protein	Carbs	Sugar	Fat	Sat Fat	Fibre	Fruit and Veg
493	34.6g	57.3g	11.1g	15g	5.5g	4.7g	2.4

METHOD

1. Preheat the oven to 180C/350F/Gas Mark 4. Place a pan of slightly salted water on to boil (you can boil the water in the kettle first if you'd like). Once boiling put the chips into the pan and allow to simmer for 5 minutes to par-boil. You want the chips just tender but not falling apart.

2. Mix together the mince, shallots, garlic, Worcestershire sauce with a pinch of salt and pepper in a bowl. Using your hands makes this much easier! Separate the mixture into two even lumps and form each into a ball. Put on a board/plate and gently pat each ball down slightly to form a thick, juicy burger.

3. Once the chips are ready drain and set aside to allow them to steam off any excess water. Spray a roasting tin with sunflower oil spray. Tip the chips into the tin and spray the top of them with sunflower oil, then sprinkle a little salt and pepper on top. Put the tray into the oven. The chips will need to cook for about 20 - 25 minutes, and will need turning once mid way through cooking.

4. Put a frying or griddle pan onto a medium to high heat on the hob. Brush both sides of the burgers will a little sunflower oil. When the chips are about 10 minutes away from being cooked place the burgers into the pan. The burgers will need 5-7 minutes each side, depending on how thick they are and how you like them cooked.

5. While the burgers are cooking turn the grill on to a medium heat. Slice the rolls in half and place under the grill to toast (keeping a close eye on them!).

6. Once the burgers are cooked, top with the cheese and place under the grill for a couple of minutes until the cheese is melting.

7. Serve the burger in the bun with the sliced tomato, a little of the lettuce and the ketchup with the chips on the side next to the remaining lettuce with the sliced onion as a side salad.

You can use leftover chicken from a roast for this recipe. In which case, if the chicken is already cooked, simply chop/shred it into bite size pieces and add to the mixture just before you assemble your pie.

Creamy Tarragon Chicken & Leek Pie with Cabbage

Serves 2 • **Prep** 10 mins • **Cook** 40 mins

INGREDIENTS

Chicken Breast, Skinless and Boneless – Diced into 2cm/1 inch cubes	2 Sm Breasts/200g
Leeks – Thinly sliced	1 Leek
Chicken Stock, Pre-Made	150ml
Butter	10g
Semi Skimmed Milk	35ml
Olive Oil	1 Tsp
Single Cream	3 Tbsp
Potatoes – Peeled	250g
Savoy Cabbage – Shredded	200g
Tarragon, Ground	1 Tsp
Garlic – Peeled and crushed	1 Clove
Dry White Wine	75ml
Salt	1 Pinch
Black Pepper	1 Pinch

NUTRITION INFO per Serving

Cals	Protein	Carbs	Sugar	Fat	Sat Fat	Fibre	Fruit and Veg
406	37.5g	29.5g	8.7g	12.8g	4.8g	6.9g	2

METHOD

1. Preheat the oven to 200C/400F/Gas Mark 6. Put the potatoes in a pan of water on a high heat with a pinch of salt to boil ready for mashing.

2. Put a pan on a medium heat with the olive oil and fry the diced chicken very gently until almost cooked. Add the sliced leeks and tarragon to the pan and continue to cook gently for five minutes, or until the leeks are soft.

3. When the leeks are soft, add the stock, cream, wine and garlic, season with salt and pepper, and simmer for about 10 minutes to reduce (or until the sauce is the thickness you want). Then put the mixture into an ovenproof dish.

4. When the potatoes are cooked, mash them with the butter and milk, season to taste with a little pepper. Spread the mash on top of the chicken mixture and fluff the top with a fork to ensure a crispy topping. Cook in oven until the topping is lightly browned (about 15 minutes).

5. While the pie is cooking put the cabbage in a pan with water (coming up to about two thirds the height of the cabbage), cover with a lid and boil/steam for about 7-10 minutes until tender.

6. Drain the cabbage (season if required) and serve with the piping hot creamy chicken pie.

A firm favourite, this fish pie is simple to make and tastes delicious – much better than putting a shop bought one in the microwave.

Homemade Creamy Fish Pie

Serves 2 • **Prep** 20 mins • **Cook** 30 mins

INGREDIENTS

Salmon Fillet (Ready to Cook), Raw	1 Sm Fillet/120g
Haddock Fillet (Ready to Cook), Raw	1 Fillet/140g
White Flour	1 Tbsp
Dill, Dried	1 Tsp
Garlic – Peeled and crushed	1 Clove
Skimmed Milk	200ml
Leeks - Finely sliced	½ Leek/85g
Potatoes - Peeled and cut into similar sized chunks for mashing	200g
Butter	10g
Prawns, Peeled	100g
Onions - Finely diced	½ Med/90g
Bay Leaf	1 Leaf
Salt	1 Pinch
Black Pepper	1 Pinch
Sunflower Oil Spray	10 Sprays

NUTRITION INFO per Serving

Cals	Protein	Carbs	Sugar	Fat	Sat Fat	Fibre	Fruit and Veg
435	47.3g	32.5g	9.6g	12.9g	4.3g	3.2g	0.9

METHOD

1. Put the potatoes in a pan of lightly salted water and bring to the boil. Cook for 15 minutes or until tender enough for mashing.

2. Heat the milk and bay leaf in a pan and add the salmon, prawns and haddock to poach for about 10 minutes or until the fish is cooked through. Preheat the oven to 180°C/350°F/Gas Mark 4.

3. Put a frying pan on a medium heat with the oil and add the leek and onion. Sauté gently until the leeks become tender (about 5 minutes). Add the garlic for the last couple of minutes of cooking.

4. Remove the poached fish from the milk with a slotted spoon and pull apart the haddock and salmon gently with a fork to make bite sized pieces. Place the fish into a rectangular ovenproof dish with the cooked vegetables. Remove the bay leaf from the milk.

5. In the frying pan melt the butter, add the flour and stir vigorously to make a roux. Slowly add the fish milk (reserving 3-4 tablespoons of the milk for the mash), stirring continuously to make the sauce. Add the dill to the sauce and stir in. Allow the sauce to simmer, stirring frequently, to thicken up.

6. Mash the potatoes with the remaining milk and season with a pinch of salt and pepper.

7. Pour the sauce over the fish. Then spread the mash over the top. Using a fork make the surface of the potato rough (this will help the potato to come out nice and crispy).

8. Cook in the oven for about 15-20 minutes or until the potato topping is crispy and golden brown.

Serve with veg of your choice (we like fine green beans or cabbage), or with a green side salad.

Comfort food at its best! Warming and filling, this is a great one to make ahead and stock up the freezer with.

Homemade Cottage Pie

Serves 2 • **Prep** 10 mins • **Cook** 40 mins

INGREDIENTS

Onions - Finely chopped	½ Sm Onion/90g
Celery - Thinly sliced	1 Stalk/40g
Potatoes - Peeled and cut into similar chunks for mashing	300g
Semi Skimmed Milk	75ml
Butter	15g
Salt	1 Pinch
Black Pepper	1 Pinch
Beef Mince, Extra Lean	300g
Vegetable Oil	2 Tsp
Beef Stock Cube	1 Cube
Mixed Herbs, Dried	¼ Tsp
Carrots - Peeled and finely diced	1 Carrot/75g

NUTRITION INFO per Serving

Cals	Protein	Carbs	Sugar	Fat	Sat Fat	Fibre	Fruit and Veg
439	37.3g	30.9g	6.2g	19.8g	7.7g	3.2g	0.9

METHOD

1. Put the grill on to a medium heat. Place the potatoes in a pan of slightly salted water to boil and allow to cook for about 15 minutes (or until tender enough for mashing).

2. While the potatoes are cooking, heat the oil in a large based frying or saucepan. Fry the mince (starting slowly to release fat) until it is browned, breaking up any lumps, then add the onion, carrots and celery and continue to cook for 5 minutes.

3. Add 100 ml boiling water, the (crumbled) stock cube and the mixed herbs, then stir, cover and simmer whilst you cook the potatoes. (If the mixture starts to get too dry add a little more water.

4. Drain and mash the potatoes with the milk and butter, season with salt and pepper to taste.

5. Transfer the beef mixture to a rectangular ovenproof dish, spread the mashed potatoes over the top, and fluff the surface with a fork.

6. Grill until golden brown (about 5-7 minutes), then serve.

Serve with your favourite steamed vegetables, this is particularly tasty with broccoli or green beans.

A fantastic, filling soup that's great if you've got some leftover roast chicken. If not a shop bought roasted chicken breast works fine (or you can roast your own for this recipe).

Chicken & Corn Chowder

Serves 4 • **Prep** 20 mins • **Cook** 30 mins

INGREDIENTS

Olive Oil	2 Tsp
Onions – Finely chopped	1 Med/180g
White Flour	30g
Semi Skimmed Milk	250ml
Water	500ml
White Potatoes – Peeled and chopped into 1cm cubes	300g
Chicken Stock Cube	1 Cube
Roasted Chicken Breast with skin removed	2 Breasts/205g
Sweetcorn	200g
Salt	1 Pinch
Black pepper	1 Pinch

NUTRITION INFO per Serving

Cals	Protein	Carbs	Sugar	Fat	Sat Fat	Fibre	Fruit and Veg
288	20g	35.5g	10.1g	7.5g	2g	2.7g	1.2

METHOD

1. Heat the oil in a large heavy based pan. Add the chopped onion and fry gently until just starting to colour. Make the stock cube up with 250ml water. Heat the milk and add to the stock.

2. Add the flour to the pan and stir continuously for a minute or so. Remove the pan from the heat and stir in the stock, adding a little at a time.

3. Return to the heat and bring to the boil. Season to taste with salt and pepper.

4. Add the chicken, potatoes and sweetcorn. Lower the heat, cover and simmer for 25-30 minutes (or until the potatoes are tender and the thickness of the soup is to your liking).

5. Check the seasoning and serve.

For around another 140 calories you can enjoy your chowder with a crusty roll.

Chilli Beef Stir Fry
with Rice

Serves 2 • **Prep** 30 mins • **Cook** 20 mins

INGREDIENTS

Five Spice Powder	½ Tsp
Basmati Rice	100g
Fresh Ginger – Peeled and finely chopped or grated	1 Tsp
Garlic – Peeled and crushed	2 Cloves
Red Chilli Pepper – De-seeded and finely chopped	1 Sm Pepper/13g
Red Pepper – De-seeded and sliced into strips	1 Med/160g
Mange Tout/Sugar Snap Peas	100g
Cornflour	1 Tsp/5g
Sirloin Steak – Visible fat removed and sliced into thin strips	200g
Black pepper	1 Pinch
Sunflower Oil Spray	10 Sprays
Soy Sauce	2 Tbsp
Rice Wine or Sake	1 Tbsp
Chicken Stock Cube	¼ Cube
Spring Onions – Finely sliced	2 Med/30g

NUTRITION INFO per Serving

Cals	Protein	Carbs	Sugar	Fat	Sat Fat	Fibre	Fruit and Veg
396	31.5g	51.7g	8.4g	6.1g	2.2g	3.9g	1.9

METHOD

1. Mix 1 tablespoon of the soy sauce with the rice wine, the 5 spice powder and a pinch of black pepper. Put the sliced beef into a bowl with the mixture and marinade for at least 30 minutes. The longer you can marinade the beef for the better! You can even leave the beef marinating overnight.

2. Cook the rice as per the packet instructions. Put a wok or large heavy based pan on a high heat on the hob.

3. Use a quarter of a chicken stock cube to make up 100ml of stock and dissolve the cornflour in a little water (about a tablespoon).

4. Spray some oil into the wok and stir fry the ginger and garlic for a minute on their own. Then add the peppers, onions and mange tout. Add a little water to the pan to help soften the vegetables instead of using more oil.

5. Add the beef strips (including the marinade) to the pan and stir fry for a minute or two until the beef is browned and cooked to your liking.

6. Add the chicken stock, the remaining soy sauce, and the cornflour to thicken.

7. Drain the rice and fluff through with a fork. Serve the chilli beef over the rice - making sure you scrape all the saucy goodness from the pan.

If you can get it, use undyed cooked smoked haddock for this recipe. If you enjoy this dish you could also try substituting the haddock for smoked mackerel.

Smoked Haddock & Leek
Chowder

Serves 4 • **Prep** 15 mins • **Cook** 40 mins

INGREDIENTS

Potatoes – Peeled and diced into small chunks	500g
Leeks – Cut into round slices about ½cm thick	1 Leek/165g
Celery – Chopped into small pieces	2 Stalks/80g
Vegetable Stock Cube	1 Cube
Water	½ Pint/284ml
Semi Skimmed Milk	1 Pint/568ml
Smoked Haddock Fillets	300g
Sweetcorn	350g
Carrots – Peeled and cut into small chunks	2 Carrots/150g
Olive Oil Spray	5 Sprays
Unsmoked Back Bacon – Diced into small pieces	2 Rashers/64g
Bay Leaves	2 Leaves
Salt	1 Pinch
Black Pepper	1 Pinch

NUTRITION INFO per Serving

Cals	Protein	Carbs	Sugar	Fat	Sat Fat	Fibre	Fruit and Veg
403	30.9g	50.1g	17.4g	9.1g	3.4g	5.2g	2.2

METHOD

1. Place the milk in pan with two bay leaves. Bring to a gentle boil then cover, and turn the heat off to allow the bay to infuse. Make up the vegetable stock with half a pint (280ml) of boiling water.

2. In a large, heavy based saucepan spray a little oil and add the chopped bacon. Cook on a medium heat until the bacon is browned. Add the leeks, celery, potatoes and carrots and season with salt and pepper. Stir together and continue to cook through for about five minutes or until the vegetables begin to soften.

3. Remove the bay leaves from the milk and pour the milk and stock into the pan. Add the potatoes, bring to the boil and simmer until the vegetables are cooked through but still have a little bite. Add the corn. You can thicken the soup by vigorously stirring in a little flour and allowing to continue to cook for another 5-10 minutes, or thin the soup with some more boiling water if you want a thinner chowder.

4. Flake the haddock into large chunks and stir carefully into the chowder. Check and adjust the seasoning if necessary before serving piping hot.

Who would have thought you could have a sumptuous pizza for less than 500 calories!

Pizza Marina
with Peppery Salad
Serves 2 • **Prep** 30 mins • **Cook** 30 mins

INGREDIENTS

Pre-Made Pizza Base	150g
Anchovies Canned in Oil – Roughly chopped	2 Anchovies
Mozzarella Cheese – Ripped into small pieces	80g
Prawns, Peeled and cooked	100g
Mussels, Cooked	100g
Tomato Puree	2 Tbsp
Black Pepper	1 Pinch
Rocket	160g
Passata	300g
Oregano, Dried	½ Tsp
Black Olives, Pitted – Finely sliced	3 Olives
Salt	1 Pinch
Lamb's Lettuce	160g
Pickled Gherkins	2 Gherkins/70g
Cherry Tomatoes	5 Tomatoes/75g
Roasted Red Peppers in Brine – Finely chopped	150g

NUTRITION INFO per Serving

Cals	Protein	Carbs	Sugar	Fat	Sat Fat	Fibre	Fruit and Veg
495	31.4g	60.9g	14.9g	13.8g	6.9g	4.3g	4.8

METHOD

1. Heat the oven to 200°C/400°F/Gas Mark 6.

2. Put the passata, red peppers, tomato puree and oregano into a saucepan. Stir and simmer for 10 minutes, season to taste with a pinch of salt and pepper.

3. Once cooked, spread the sauce over pizza base and top with the prawns and mussels. Sprinkle over the chopped anchovy and olives, top with the cheese.

4. Bake in the oven for 15-25 minutes until cheese melts.

5. To serve arrange the rocket and lambs lettuce leaves onto half of your plates. Slice the cherry tomatoes in half and add to the salad. Either thinly slice the gherkins and add to the salad or slice into half lengthways and serve on the side. Once the pizza is cooked, slice in half and add one half to each plate.

Something a little bit different! Suitable for vegetarians you can easily multiply the ingredients up to make a big pot.

Spicy African Sweet Potato Stew

Serves 2 • **Prep** 20 mins • **Cook** 45 mins

INGREDIENTS

Sweet Potato – Peeled and chopped into 1 inch/2cm cubes	150g
Passata	150g
Peanut Butter, Smooth	30g
Onions – Peeled and finely chopped	1 Sm Onion/90g
Olive Oil	1½ Tbsp
Garlic – Peeled and crushed	1 Clove
Ginger Root – Peeled and very finely chopped	1 Tsp
Ground Cayenne Pepper	¼ Tsp
Baby Spinach	100g
Button Mushrooms	100g
Fresh Coriander Leaves – Finely chopped	10g
Vegetable Stock Cubes	1 Cube
Curry Paste	1 Tbsp
Salt	1 Pinch
Black Pepper	1 Pinch

NUTRITION INFO per Serving

Cals	Protein	Carbs	Sugar	Fat	Sat Fat	Fibre	Fruit and Veg
332	9.7g	26.2g	8.1g	21.2g	3.1g	5.6g	2.9

METHOD

1. Heat 1 tbsp of the oil in a pan. Add the onion, garlic, ginger and cayenne pepper and fry gently for 10 mins. Make up the stock cube with 1 pint of boiling water.

2. Add the curry paste to the onion mixture and cook, stirring, for 1 min. Add the sweet potatoes, stir to coat with the onion mixture and fry for 3-4 minutes. Add the passata and stock. Bring to the boil, cover simmer for 15-20 minutes until the sweet potatoes are almost tender.

3. Heat the remaining oil in a frying pan, add the mushrooms and stir fry for 4-5 minutes until beginning to release their juices. Add to the stew with the spinach and cook for a further 5 minutes or until the vegetables are cooked through.

4. Mix a few spoonfuls of the stew juices with the peanut butter to soften it slightly and then stir back into the pan. Add the coriander, season with salt and pepper to taste. Serve garnished with coriander sprigs.

You can serve this with a toasted pitta bread each for an extra 160 calories per person.

A warm reception for a hungry family. Especially good when cooked the day before and reheated. Make sure it is piping hot if you are reheating.

Lamb Stew

Serves 4 • **Prep** 15 mins • **Cook** 50 mins

INGREDIENTS

Garlic – Peeled and crushed	1 Clove
Lamb Neck or Shoulder, Visible Fat Removed – Diced into 1 inch/2cm chunks	450g
Potatoes – Peeled and diced into bite size pieces	450g
Carrots – Peeled and diced into bite size pieces	6 Carrots/450g
Onions - Roughly sliced	1 Med/180g
Bay Leaves	3 Leaves
White Flour	2 Tbsp
Lamb Stock Cubes	2 Cubes
Thyme, Fresh	3 Sprigs
Salt	1 Pinch
Black pepper	1 Pinch
Vegetable Oil	1 Tbsp

NUTRITION INFO per Serving

Cals	Protein	Carbs	Sugar	Fat	Sat Fat	Fibre	Fruit and Veg
383	27.6g	36.1g	10	14.6g	5.2g	4.7g	2.2

METHOD

1. Heat the oil in a heavy based pan on the hob on a medium heat. Mix the lamb pieces with the flour and a pinch of salt and pepper in a bowl to coat, then cook the lamb in the pan until browned all over. Add the garlic and cook for a further minute.

2. Make up the stock with 2 pints of boiling water and add 3/4 of the stock to the pan stirring to incorporate any flour stuck to the pan.

3. Add the carrots, onions, potatoes bay leaves and thyme, and bring to the boil, stirring regularly.

4. When the gravy has thickened, cover and simmer for approximately 30 minutes, or until the potatoes and meat are tender. Add some of the remaining stock throughout cooking if necessary.

Serve with fresh steamed vegetables such as broccoli and cauliflower. You can also add a chunk of fresh crusty bread for around an extra 150 calories per person.

Sticky Lemon Chicken
with Egg Fried Rice

Serves 2 • **Prep** 35 mins • **Cook** 35 mins

INGREDIENTS

Chicken Breast, Skinless and Boneless	2 Breasts/240g
Clear Honey	1 Tbsp
Lemon Juice	3 Tbsp
Dry White Wine	2 Tbsp
Dried Ground Thyme	¼ Tsp
Ground Ginger	¼ Tsp
Garlic – Peeled and crushed	1 Clove
White Rice	2 Servings/100g
Frozen Peas	50g
Medium Eggs	2 Eggs
Sunflower Oil Spray	5 Sprays

You can make this look fit for a dinner party by using cups to mould the rice (fill a cup with the cooked rice then upturn onto the plate), and adding slices of fresh lemon to garnish the chicken when served on the plate.

NUTRITION INFO per Serving

Cals	Protein	Carbs	Sugar	Fat	Sat Fat	Fibre	Fruit and Veg
491	45.8g	51.4g	9.2g	10.3g	2.5g	1.4g	0.7

METHOD

1. Put the garlic, honey, lemon juice, white wine, thyme and ginger into a small container with a lid. Shake until well blended.

2. Put the chicken breasts into a small casserole dish and pour over the marinade. Cover the dish and leave to marinate for 30-60 minutes.

3. Put a pan of water on the hob to boil and cook the rice as per the pack instructions (it doesn't matter if this is ready ahead of time as you are going to stir fry it at the last minute). During the last few minutes of cooking add the peas to the rice pan.

4. Preheat the oven to 190C/375F/gas mark 5.

5. Bake the Chicken in the oven, covered, for 25 minutes. Remove from the oven, take off the lid and baste the chicken with the marinade. Return to the oven and cook uncovered for a further 5-10 minutes to reduce the marinade.

6. While the chicken is cooking for it's last few minutes put a wok (or large saucepan on a high heat on the hob. Coat the pan with the spray oil.

7. Add the rice to the pan and make a well in the centre, pour in the egg and mix quickly until the egg is cooked through. This will be a very quick process.

8. Take the rice off the heat and serve with the chicken, spooning over any remaining sticky lemon sauce from the dish.

Get a fantastic nutrient hit with this simple chicken dish – 8 of you five a day!

Chicken Pomodoro
with Green Vegetables

Serves 1 • **Prep** 20 mins • **Cook** 1 hr 10 mins

INGREDIENTS

Thyme, Dried	1 Tsp
Garlic – Peeled and crushed	1 Clove
Worcestershire Sauce	1 Tsp
Chopped Tomatoes, Canned	1 Can/400g
Mushrooms –Peeled and sliced	50g
Olive Oil	1 Tsp
Onions – Peeled and finely diced	½ Sm Onion/90g
Mozzarella Cheese - Grated	25g
Chicken Thighs, Skinless	2 Thighs/180g
Salt	1 Pinch
Black Pepper	1 Pinch
Broccoli	130g

NUTRITION INFO per Serving

Cals	Protein	Carbs	Sugar	Fat	Sat Fat	Fibre	Fruit and Veg
495	52.3g	21.7g	15.6g	22.2g	4.2g	8.3g	8.3

METHOD

1. Preheat the oven to 180C/350F/Gas Mark 4. Heat the olive oil in a pan on a medium heat. Sauté the onions, mushrooms and garlic in the oil.

2. Season the chicken thighs with a pinch of salt and pepper and gently brown in the pan with the onion and garlic.

3. Add the tomatoes, thyme and Worcestershire sauce to the pan and stir.

4. Place the chicken and sauce in a casserole dish and put in the oven. Cook for about 45 minutes (or until the chicken is cooked through).

5. Just before the chicken is ready, boil or steam the broccoli for about 5-7 minutes until tender. (You can substitute the broccoli with another vegetable if you like - try fine green beans, cauliflower or asparagus).

6. While the broccoli is cooking, remove the chicken from the oven and sprinkle the cheese on top. Return to the oven for 3-5 minutes until the cheese is bubbling.

Serve the chicken with your veg, or a green salad if you'd prefer.

A longer cooking time really reaps rewards with this rich and interesting Eastern inspired lamb dish. It also gives you all of your 5 a day!

Moroccan Spiced Lamb

Serves 2 • **Prep** 10 mins • **Cook** 1 hr 30 mins

INGREDIENTS

Lamb Leg Steak – Visible fat removed and cut into 1 inch/2cm chunks	200g
White Flour	15g
Dried Apricots – Roughly chopped	3 Apricots/30g
Water	150ml
Ground Cinnamon	¼ Tsp
Ground Cumin	½ Tsp
Paprika	½ Tsp
Ground Coriander Seeds	½ Tsp
Onions – Peeled and roughly chopped	½ Med/90g
Garlic – Peeled and crushed	1 Clove
Red Peppers – De-seeded and chopped into bite size pieces	1 Med/160g
Courgette – Sliced into 1cm rounds then halved	1 Courgette/224g
Chopped Tomatoes, Canned	1 Can/400g
Fresh Mint – Finely chopped	1 Tbsp
Lamb Stock Cubes	1 Cube
Basmati Rice	100g
Sunflower Oil Spray	10 Sprays
Sunflower Oil	1 Tsp
Salt	1 Pinch
Black Pepper	1 Pinch
Greek Yoghurt, 0% Fat	30g

METHOD

1. Place the lamb in a plastic bag with the flour, cinnamon, cumin, paprika and coriander. Shake the bag well to coat the lamb with a dusting of spices.

2. Heat the teaspoon of sunflower oil in a large, non-stick frying pan, add the lamb and cook for 5 minutes, stirring until it is browned on all sides. If you need more oil to keep the pan greased use a spray oil.

3. Add the onion, garlic, pepper, courgettes, apricots, chopped tomatoes and stock and bring to the boil. Season to taste with salt and pepper. Reduce the heat, cover and simmer for 1 hour.

4. Just before the final stage with the lamb, cook the rice as per pack instructions.

5. Remove the cover from the pan. Turn up the heat and allow the sauce to bubble quite hard for around 10-15 minutes to reduce the sauce to the thickness you like. Take care to stir occasionally at this point so the lamb doesn't catch on the bottom of the pan.

Serve over the fluffed rice, with a dollop of yoghurt on top then sprinkle over the fresh mint.

NUTRITION INFO per Serving

Cals	Protein	Carbs	Sugar	Fat	Sat Fat	Fibre	Fruit and Veg
500	33.6g	70.7g	21.1g	8.7g	2.5g	6g	5.9

A perfect combination of fruit, vegetables and low fat meat, these kebabs are delicious cooked on the barbecue in summer, and equally as tempting when cooked under a hot grill in the winter.

Hawaiian Kebabs

Serves 2 • **Prep** 15 mins • **Marinate** 1 hour • **Cook** 20 mins

INGREDIENTS

Button Mushrooms – Peeled, left whole	50g
Cherry Tomatoes – Left whole	8 Tomatoes/120g
Black Pepper	½ Tsp
English Mustard	½ Tsp
Ground Ginger	½ Tsp
Garlic – Peeled and crushed	1 Clove
Soft Brown Sugar	½ Tsp
Pineapple Juice	60ml
Chicken Breasts, Skinless and Boneless – Diced into bitesize chunks	2 Sm Breasts/200g
Red Pepper – De-seeded and cut into chunks	1 Med/160g
Pineapple (fresh or canned) – Diced into 1 inch cubes	100g
Soy Sauce	3 Tbsp
Green Salad Leaves	200g

NUTRITION INFO per Serving

Cals	Protein	Carbs	Sugar	Fat	Sat Fat	Fibre	Fruit and Veg
235	30.9g	21.4g	19g	3g	0.7g	2.7g	3.5

METHOD

If using wooden skewers ensure that they have been soaked in cold water for at least a few minutes before cooking to prevent charring.

1. Make the marinade by mixing the pineapple juice, soy sauce, sugar, garlic, ginger, mustard and pepper together in a small saucepan over a low heat. Bring the mixture to the boil and simmer for 5 minutes to reduce, then leave to cool (5-10 minutes).

3. Pour the marinade over the chicken in a bowl, cover and chill for at least 1 hour in the bottom of the refrigerator.

4. Thread the marinated chicken onto skewers along with the prepared vegetables and pineapple, pop a cherry tomato on each end of each skewer and grill for about 20 minutes, turning and basting frequently with the marinade.

Serve with a green salad and be careful when biting into the tomatoes!

For an extra 100 calories you can add 150g boiled new potatoes.

Authentic Chicken Balti
with Rice

Serves 2 • **Prep** 10 mins • **Cook** 1 hr 30 mins

INGREDIENTS

Onion – Peeled and chopped into chunks	1 Med/180g
Garlic – Peeled and crushed	2 Cloves
Fresh Ginger – Peeled and finely chopped	1 Tbsp
Ground Coriander Seeds	½ Tsp
Ground Cumin Seeds	½ Tsp
Curry Powder	½ Tsp
Paprika	½ Tsp
Turmeric Powder	½ Tsp
Ground Garam Masala	½ Tsp
Ground Ginger	¼ Tsp
Salt	1 Pinch
Chilli Powder	½ Tsp
Chopped Tomatoes, Canned	½ Can/200g
Chicken Breast, Skinless and Boneless – Cut into fairly large chunks	2 Small Breasts/200g
Basmati Rice	100g
Vegetable Oil	2 Tsp
Tomato Puree	2 Tbsp
Tomatoes – Roughly chopped into large chunks	2 Tomatoes/240g
Cornflour	1 Tsp

NUTRITION INFO per Serving

Cals	Protein	Carbs	Sugar	Fat	Sat Fat	Fibre	Fruit and Veg
479	37.2g	63.7g	14.8g	9g	1.3g	4.6g	4.5

METHOD

1. Heat the oil in a large pan over a low to medium heat. Add all the spices to the pan with the tomato puree and stir for about 30 seconds to bring out the flavours. Add the onion, fresh ginger and garlic to the pan and stir. Add a little water (about 100ml). Simmer very gently for about 15 minutes, stirring so the mixture does not catch on the bottom of the pan.

2. Add the canned chopped tomatoes and another 200ml of water and allow to simmer for about 10 minutes (stirring occasionally). Make the cornflour into a paste with a tablespoon or two of cold water. Add the cornflour slowly, stirring continuously to thicken the sauce.

3. Add the chicken and allow to simmer for 45-60 minutes until the meat is cooked through and tender. You may need to top up with a little water throughout cooking to ensure the meat is covered. About half way through cooking the meat add the fresh tomatoes.

4. When you are about 20 minutes away from serving cook the rice as per pack instructions.

Serve the balti with the cooked, fluffed rice.

A taste of India – This curry is even better if cooked the day before and re-heated. It can also be frozen for times when you want a quick meal with minimal effort.

A French classic that's great for all the family. Particularly good when the nights get a little colder and you have comfort food cravings.

Beef Bourguignon
with New Potatoes

Serves 4 • **Prep** 15 mins • **Cook** 2 hrs

INGREDIENTS

Onions	1 Med/180g
– Peeled and chopped into large chunks	
Dried Marjoram	½ Tsp
Dried Thyme	½ Tsp
Olive Oil	2 Tsp
Sirloin Steak – Cut into 1 inch/2cm cubes	400g
Red Wine	125ml
Button Mushrooms – Wiped and left whole	200g
Beef Stock Cubes	2 Cubes
Plain White Flour	2 Tbsp
New Potatoes	600g
Salt	1 Pinch
Pepper	1 Pinch

NUTRITION INFO per Serving

Cals	Protein	Carbs	Sugar	Fat	Sat Fat	Fibre	Fruit and Veg
415	27g	36.4g	4.5g	16.3g	6.2g	3g	1.3

METHOD

1. Cook the onions in half the olive oil until translucent, and put to one side. Make up the stock cubes to 2 pints with boiling water.

2. Toss the beef in the flour with a pinch of salt and pepper to coat. In a large heavy based pan heat the remaining oil then gently cook the meat until brown, stirring to prevent sticking and cook for 1 minute.

3. Sprinkle on marjoram and thyme and stir well.

4. Add the wine and enough stock to cover meat and stir to ensure the flour and liquid are fully incorporated. Cover the pan and simmer on low heat for about 1½ hours, checking regularly and adding more stock if necessary to keep meat covered.

5. Add the mushrooms and onion to the meat and cook for a further 20 minutes, stirring occasionally and adding small amounts of liquid if too thick, although the gravy should be thick like a sauce. While the bourguinon finishes cooking boil the new potatoes until tender (about 20 minutes).

Serve the beef with the new potatoes. You could even add some fine green beans or steamed cabbage.

This dish takes a little longer to cook but is definitely worth it – strong smooth flavours make a great meal from the cheaper cut of beef.

Beef Goulash
with Rice

Serves 2 • **Prep** 20 mins • **Cook** 2 hrs

INGREDIENTS

Chopped Tomatoes, Canned	½ Can/200g
Tomato Puree	2 Tsp
Red Pepper	1 Med/160g
– De-seeded and chopped into chunks	
Button Mushrooms – Wiped and cut into halves	100g
Plain Yoghurt, Low Fat	30g
Onions – Peeled and roughly chopped	½ Med/90g
Garlic – Peeled and crushed	1 Clove
Paprika	1 Tsp
Beef Stock Cube	1 Cube
Cornflour	2 Tsp
Beef Braising Steak	250g
– Visible fat removed and cut into 1 inch cubes	
Vegetable Oil	1 Tsp
White Rice	2 Servings/100g
Salt	1 Pinch
Pepper	1 Pinch

NUTRITION INFO per Serving

Cals	Protein	Carbs	Sugar	Fat	Sat Fat	Fibre	Fruit and Veg
491	39.9g	58.1g	11.4g	11.1g	3.2g	3.4g	3.5

METHOD

1. Make up the stock cube with 1 pint of boiling water and set aside.

2. Heat the oil in large pan and gently fry the onion for 3 minutes.

3. Add the beef and fry on high heat for 4-5 minutes until browned, stirring regularly.

4. Turn down the heat, add the garlic and paprika, and fry gently for a further minute. Stir in the tomatoes, tomato puree, peppers and mushrooms; continue to cook for 2 minutes, stirring frequently. Stir in the stock, season to taste with salt and pepper then bring to the boil. Cover and simmer gently for 1½ to 2 hours.

5. When the goulash is about 20 minutes away from being ready, cook the rice according to pack instructions.

6. 5 minutes before serving, blend the corn flour with 30ml of water and add to the Goulash, stirring continuously until goulash is thickened and smooth. Remove the goulash from the heat, stir in the yoghurt, and serve with the rice.

Something a little different to try. With Spanish influences this dish is great for sitting in the garden in the summer.

Chorizo and Bean Hotpot

Serves 2 • **Prep** 20 mins • **Cook** 2 hrs

INGREDIENTS

Red Onion - Finely diced	1 Sm/90g
Garlic – Peeled and finely sliced	2 Cloves
Chorizo Sausage - Cut to 1cm slices	160g
Butter Beans, Canned, Drained	120g
Red Kidney Beans, Canned, Drained	½ Can/90g
Chopped Tomatoes, Canned	1 Can/400g
Savoy Cabbage - Shredded	200g
Parmesan Cheese - Finely grated	2 Tbsp
Vegetable Stock Cube	1 Cube
Olive Oil	1 Tsp
Salt	1 Pinch
Black Pepper	1 Pinch

NUTRITION INFO per Serving

Cals	Protein	Carbs	Sugar	Fat	Sat Fat	Fibre	Fruit and Veg
496	32.7g	34.1g	13.7g	26.6g	0.7g	10.9g	6

METHOD

1. Heat the oil in a large pan over a low to medium heat. Add the onion and sweat gently. Add the chorizo and stir. Once some of the oils from the chorizo have been released (about a minute) add the garlic and leave to cook gently for about 5 minutes (the onion should be soft, not brown and 'fried').

2. Add the chopped tomatoes and the beans.

3. Make up the vegetable stock cube to 1 pint with boiling water and pour two thirds of the stock into the pan. Season to taste with salt and pepper.

4. Let the hotpot simmer gently on a low heat for 1-2 hours so the flavours develop. You can top up with the remaining stock if necessary.

5. 15 minutes before serving add the cabbage to the pot.

6. Serve sprinkled with some freshly grated parmesan.

This can be reheated the next day (tastes even better), or made in batches which you can freeze.

A sweet and sticky taste of Japan without the cost (in pounds or calories) of a takeaway. Making these types of dishes at home can really help you to control your waistline (and the purse-strings)!

Teriyaki Pork Steaks
with Rice

Serves 2 • **Prep** 2 hrs • **Cook** 25 mins

INGREDIENTS

Sugar	½ Tsp
Sherry or Rice Wine (Sake)	1 Tbsp
Garlic – Peeled and crushed	1 Clove
Ginger Root – Peeled and very finely chopped	1 Tbsp
Soy Sauce	1 Tbsp
White Rice	100g
Sesame Oil	1 Tsp
Sesame Seeds	1 Tsp
Pork Loin Steaks – Visible fat removed	2 Sm Steaks/250g

NUTRITION INFO per Serving

Cals	Protein	Carbs	Sugar	Fat	Sat Fat	Fibre	Fruit and Veg
488	33.3g	45g	1.4g	18.9g	5.5g	1g	0.1

METHOD

1. To make the marinade combine the soy sauce, sugar, sherry, oil, ginger and garlic.

2. Put the pork into a plastic bag and pour in the marinade, shaking to mix, and then put in refrigerator for at least an hour (the longer you can leave the pork to marinate, the better - even overnight!)

3. To cook the dish, turn the grill onto a medium heat or light the barbeque. Remove the pork and reserve the marinade.

4. Grill or barbecue the pork with a medium heat for about 25 minutes turning half way through. Brush each side of the pork two or three more times with the reserved marinade while cooking.

5. While the pork is grilling, cook the rice as per the pack instructions.

6. Leave the pork to stand for 5 minutes after sprinkling the sesame seeds on top, and then slice diagonally into thin slices.

Serve the pork slices on top of the fluffed up rice. You could add some steamed Mange Tout or Broccoli to this dish.

A great dish for the whole family, the crispy potatoes on top of this hotpot will be a real winner. This can be served with almost any vegetable combination to make a bit of a change.

Lancashire Hotpot

Serves 4 • **Prep** 30 mins • **Cook** 2 hrs

INGREDIENTS

Onions - Finely sliced	1 Med/180g
Carrots – Finely diced	3 Carrots/180g
Potatoes – Peeled and thinly sliced	2 Potatoes/360g
Lamb, Neck or Shoulder – Visible fat removed and cut into 1 inch/2cm cubes	500g
Pearl Barley	1oz/28g
Pickled Red Cabbage	200g
Celery – Finely sliced	2 Stalks/80g
Butter	25g
Vegetable Oil	2 Tsp
Salt	1 Pinch
Black pepper	1 Pinch
Lamb Stock Cubes	1 Cube
Water	450ml

NUTRITION INFO per Serving

Cals	Protein	Carbs	Sugar	Fat	Sat Fat	Fibre	Fruit and Veg
433	15.3g	31.8g	3g	27.3g	13.1g	5.1g	2.1

METHOD

1. Preheat the oven to 160C/325F/Gas Mark 3. Heat the vegetable oil in a frying pan and brown the meat quickly in the pan with a pinch of salt and pepper (substitute the salt for celery salt if you have some). Remove the meat and set aside.

2. In the oil that remains sweat down the onions, carrots and celery until soft (about 10 minutes).

3. Transfer both the meat and the vegetables to a rectangular ovenproof dish. Make up the stock with 450ml boiling water and add enough to the dish to just cover the contents with an additional 1-2cm above. Add the pearl barley and gently mix.

4. Layer the potatoes across the top of the casserole dish and cover.

5. Cook in the oven with a lid on (if you don't have an oven proof dish with a lid you can cover with foil), for one and a half hours.

6. After this time remove lid and turn the oven up to 180 degrees. Dot the butter around on top of the potatoes and cook for a further 30 minutes or until potatoes are crisp and golden brown.

Serve hot with a portion of pickled cabbage.

A great dish to cook for the family when the night's start getting colder and darker. Cooked for WLR staff members children as 'Cowboy Casserole'.

Warming Sausage Casserole
with Rice

Serves 4 • **Prep** 1 hr 30 mins • **Cook** 1 hr 30 mins

INGREDIENTS

Red Onions – Peeled and roughly chopped	1 Med/180g
Garlic – Peeled and crushed	1 Clove
Olive Oil	1 Tbsp
Chipolata Sausages	8 Chipolatas/250g
Back Bacon – Visible fat removed and diced	4 Rashers/100g
Paprika	½ Tsp
Chopped Tomatoes, Canned	400g
Chicken Stock Cubes	1 Cube
Water	200ml
Tomato Puree	1 Tbsp
Worcestershire Sauce	1 Tbsp
Dark Brown Sugar	1 Tsp
Mixed Herbs, Dried	½ Tsp
Bay Leaves	1 Leaf
Fresh Thyme	2 Sprigs
Butter Beans, Canned, Drained	1 Sm Can/125g
White Rice	200g
Salt	1 Pinch
Black Pepper	1 Pinch

METHOD

1. Heat a tablespoon of the oil in a large non-stick frying pan and fry the sausages gently for 10 minutes, turning every now and then until nicely browned all over. Transfer the sausages to a large saucepan or an ovenproof casserole dish and set aside, leaving the oil in the pan.

2. Fry the onions in the remaining oil/juices over a medium heat for around five minutes until they start to soften, then add the bacon pieces. Stir in the garlic, tomato puree and paprika and cook for a couple more minutes. Make up the stock cube with 200ml boiling water.

3. Stir in the tomatoes, stock, Worcestershire sauce, sugar, herbs and bay leaves. Add a little more water at this point if required, then add the mixture to the dish with the sausages and return to a simmer. Reduce the heat, cover the pan loosely with a lid (or foil) and leave to simmer gently for about 20 minutes, stirring from time to time. Check the seasoning and add a little salt and pepper to taste.

4. Cook the rice as per the pack instructions.

5. Drain the beans and stir into the sausage dish. Cook for 10 minutes, until the sauce is thick.

Serve the casserole with the fluffed rice. This dish also goes well with a jacket spud.

NUTRITION INFO per Serving

Cals	Protein	Carbs	Sugar	Fat	Sat Fat	Fibre	Fruit and Veg
500	22.2g	60.1g	9.4g	19.3g	6.7g	5.9g	2.4

Who would have thought that the humble apple crumble could be reinvented... at less than 200 calories per serving you can afford to treat yourself with this one!

Apple Crumble Crisp

Serves 4 • **Prep** 15 mins • **Cook** 30 mins

INGREDIENTS

Cooking Apples	200g
Sunflower Oil Spray	5 Sprays
Soft Brown Sugar	25g
Ground Cinnamon	¼ Tsp
Oats (porridge Oats)	75g
Sugar	1 Tbsp
Plain Flour	25g
Butter	25g

NUTRITION INFO per Serving

Cals	Protein	Carbs	Sugar	Fat	Sat Fat	Fibre	Fruit and Veg
197	4g	31.3g	7.2g	6.6g	3.6g	2.8g	0.7

METHOD

1. Preheat oven to 190C/375F/Gas mark 4. Peel and chop the apples into small chunks about 1cm/½ inch.

2. Place the chopped apple evenly in a baking dish or in small single serving ovenproof dishes, spritzed with the oil spray. Top with the brown sugar and a pinch of cinnamon.

3. Combine the remainder of the ingredients in a bowl and rub in the butter until you have a crumbly texture. Add another pinch of cinnamon to this mixture.

4. Top the apples with the crumble mixture and bake in the oven for 20-30 minutes (until the apple is soft and the topping golden brown).

For an extra 80 calories per person you can add a scoop of vanilla ice cream each to serve.

Sumptuous apricots make this dish a wonderful dessert for a dinner party.

Apricot Clafoutis
Serves 4 • **Prep** 15 mins • **Cook** 30 mins

INGREDIENTS

Apricot Halves, Canned in Juice	400g
Apricot Jam, Reduced Sugar	2 Tbsp
Self Raising Flour	60g
Large Eggs	3 Eggs
Skimmed Milk	200ml
Baking Powder	1 Tsp
Ground Cinnamon	½ Tsp
Granulated Sweeteneer	4 Tbsp
Icing Sugar	1 Tsp
Sunflower Oil Spray	5 Sprays
Lemon - Zested and juiced	1 Lemon

NUTRITION INFO per Serving

Cals	Protein	Carbs	Sugar	Fat	Sat Fat	Fibre	Fruit and Veg
263	10.2g	42g	17.1g	6.1g	1.6g	1.6g	1.5

METHOD

1. Preheat the oven to 190C/375F/Gas mark 5.

2. Drain the apricots, discard the juice. Pop them in a pan with the jam and heat gently, stirring constantly until the jam melts.

3. Spray a baking tray or dish with spray oil then arrange the apricots face down. Sprinkle over the lemon juice and zest.

4. Whisk together the flour, eggs, baking powder, milk, cinnamon, and sweetener until it resembles a batter.

5. Pour the batter mixture over the apricots and bake in the oven for 25- 30 minutes, or until the mixture sets and is golden brown.

6. Dust with little icing sugar and serve warm.

For an extra 80 calories per serving you can add a scoop of vanilla ice cream for each person.

A chocolate hit for less than 100 calories - who could ask for more! These cheeky little desserts can be kept in the fridge for a few days.

Light Chocolate Mousse

Serves 6 • **Prep** 20 mins • **Cook** 2 hrs 40 mins

INGREDIENTS

Medium Eggs	4 Eggs
Powdered Gelatin	6g
Cocoa Powder	1 Tbsp
Water	120ml
Caster Sugar	65g

NUTRITION INFO per Serving

Cals	Protein	Carbs	Sugar	Fat	Sat Fat	Fibre	Fruit and Veg
98	5.1g	11.2g	9.0g	3.8g	1.1g	0.3g	0.0

METHOD

1. Boil the kettle and allow to cool slightly. Using the warm water from the kettle mix the water and gelatine powder in a jug or small bowl with a fork until the gelatine has completely dissolved. Stir in the cocoa powder and set aside to cool for 10 minutes.

2. Separate the yolks from the whites of the eggs. Beat the egg whites in a large bowl until soft peaks form. Add the sugar a little bit at a time, beating until mixture is thick and glossy. Add the egg yolks while vigorously whisking the mixture, 1 at a time, beating well after each addition.

3. Once the gelatine mixture has cooled, slowly pour the gelatine mixture into the egg mixture, beating constantly until well combined.

4. Spoon the mixture into 6 small serving dishes/glasses. Refrigerate for 4 hours or until set and chilled.

Just before serving dust with a little cocoa powder. You can add some summer berries such as strawberries to the top for serving - 3 or 4 berries are less than 5 calories.

Quick and easy, this is the ideal no fuss dessert - looks great for minimal effort. You can either make this in a very small round springform tin or, alternatively make individual portions.

No Bake Strawberry Cheesecake

Serves 2 • **Prep** 35 mins • **Cook** 2 hrs

INGREDIENTS

Oat Biscuits, Reduced Fat	50g
Margarine, Reduced Fat	15g
Leaf Gelatine	1 ½ Leaves
Soft Cheese, Extra Light	50g
Fromage Frais, Fat Free	125g
Caster Sugar	1 Tbsp
Vanilla Extract	¼ Tsp
Strawberries	80g

NUTRITION INFO per Serving

Cals	Protein	Carbs	Sugar	Fat	Sat Fat	Fibre	Fruit and Veg
249	11.6g	31.5g	18.7g	8.5g	2.3g	2.1g	0.5

METHOD

1. Crush the biscuits for the base. Place a saucepan over a medium heat and melt the margarine. Stir in the crushed biscuits. Tip into the bottom of your tin or individual dishes and press down. Pop into the fridge to set for around 30 minutes.

2. Cut up the gelatine leaves and place into a heatproof bowl (big enough to fit over a saucepan), and cover the leaves with just enough cold water. Leave to soak for 5 minutes. Set a pan of water to boil over a medium heat, then place the bowl over it, leaving the gelatine to melt, stirring occasionally. Set aside to cool a little.

3. Beat the soft cheese and the fromage frais together,then add in the sugar and vanilla. Add the gelatine and stir. Spoon over the base and chill for at least 2 hours.

4. You can slice your strawberries or cut them into quarters. Arrange the strawberries on top and put back into the fridge until completely set or ready to serve.

A true classic dish, the rich coffee flavour of Tiramisu is best served chilled, a truly indulgent dessert for less than 300 calories.

Tiramisu

Serves 2 • **Prep** 20 mins • **Cook** 1 hr

INGREDIENTS

Eggs, Whites Only	½ Egg
Icing Sugar	1 Tbsp
Quark Cheese	75g
Rum	2 Tsp
Strong Black Coffee	50ml
Trifle Sponges	4 Sponges/24g
Dark Chocolate, 70%	20g
Cocoa Powder	½ Heaped Tsp

NUTRITION INFO per Serving

Cals	Protein	Carbs	Sugar	Fat	Sat Fat	Fibre	Fruit and Veg
278	8.7g	46.5g	25.3g	5.3g	2.8g	1.7g	0.0

METHOD

1. Place a pan of water over a high heat to boil. Once boiling turn down to a low simmer. Grate the chocolate.

2. Add the egg white to a heatproof bowl (large enough to sit on top of the saucepan) and whisk until stiff peaks form. Put the bowl over the pan of barely simmering water and continue to whisk, gradually adding the icing sugar until thick and glossy. Remove from the heat.

3. In another bowl, beat the quark with the rum until smooth, then gradually fold in the egg white mixture until combined.

4. Put the coffee in a shallow bowl. Cut each trifle sponge in half lengthways to make 8 thinner sponges. Dip 4 of the sponge halves briefly in the coffee and arrange in the base of a small shallow square dish, or individual portion glasses/dishes if you prefer.

5. Spread half the quark mixture over the top of the sponges, then sprinkle with half of the grated chocolate. Repeat with another layer of coffee-dipped sponge and quark, then dust with the cocoa powder and the remaining grated chocolate.

Chill in the fridge for 1 hour before serving.

The Calorie, Carb and Fat Bible

Special Offer - £14.99 (RRP £19.99)

Essential Reference

The UK's most comprehensive calorie counter book - the Calorie Carb and Fat Bible then gives nutritional information for over 22,000 UK foods so you can easily see what's in the foods you're eating. From basics such as bread and biscuits to favourite brands and supermarket ready meals.

Easy to Use Format

Nutrient info is laid out in an easy to use way listing calories, carbohydrates, protein, fat and fibre both per serving and per 100g, making it easy to compare the foods you love the most to help you make informed choices.

Basic foods are highlighted to make them easy to find for those of you who like to cook from scratch, and Chain restaurants, take aways and cafes like Domino Pizza, Caffe Nero, Burger King, Costa, JD Wetherspoon and Pret A Manger have a section at the back so you can very quickly see the calories and fat when eating out or grabbing something on the run.

Whether you are trying to eat that little bit healthier or trying to lose weight, The Calorie, Carb and Fat Bible 2014 is a great tool and perfect ally.

How to Lose Weight

Top Dietitians Juliette Kellow BSc RD and Lyndel Costain BSc RD spill the beans on fad diets and give you the know-how and strategies needed to lose weight and keep it off. Tables and charts show you how many calories you need, how many extra you burn during exercise, your body mass index and healthy weight range.

To find out more simply go to

www.weightlossresources.co.uk/calorie-bible

or give us a call on 01733 345592